Medical Mav~~.~~ ~~~ Presents

Classroom to Clinic:

The Ultimate Guide To Help Ambitious Students Consider a Career in Health

Discover 40 amazing NHS careers that you never knew existed!

#BeMoreMaverick

TOM WARRENDER

Thanks to Megan Richards for Editing

Thanks to David Myring for Design

First Edition March 2018

1

Printed by Mixam in the UK

ISBN: 978-1-78808-424-6

For you, Dad.

Love you and miss you always.

Contents

Physiology (GREEN)

Contents

Physiology continued (GREEN)

Life Science (BLUE)

Contents

Contents

Chapter 1

Why I Wrote This Book

It was Spring 1998 and I was sitting in Mr Dooley's office. Mr Dooley was my Physics teacher… and the one teacher every student in the school feared! He was the teacher that would hear you swear from 100 paces. He would bellow from one side of the school to the other and everyone would know about it. But, Mr Dooley was the best. He gained legendary status by trading in his 70's style Montego estate car for a Subaru Impreza when he was about 60. His physics lessons were ace too.

In his office we were having a chat about my A-levels and my aspirations for the future. I had always wanted to be a doctor, but the initial prognosis from my provisional grades wasn't looking good; I was pretty much on for D's and E's across the board in Biology, Chemistry & Physics. Not quite medical school material.

The conversation inevitable turned to 'what else could I do?'. I went away and looked at lots of different courses from Physiotherapy to Nursing to Paramedic Science. But none of them seemed quite right, none of them quite "me".

At the time I had recently started to run and was training for my first ever marathon. I was loving the training routine and the science behind all of the sessions was incredible, so Sports Science seemed like a logical step for me to look at. Now I'm going to show my age a little bit, this was before a million and one other students had

Chapter 1 – Why I Wrote This Book

been through Sports Science courses around the UK, as it was not as popular 'back in my day!'

The new plan was to study Sports Science and then get a job at a top premiership football team testing, analysing and supporting their players.

Easy...

However, whilst at a University of Wolverhampton open day I came across a degree called Human Physiology & Exercise Science (top tip... go to the Uni open days! You'll never know what you will discover!). The Applied Science department were running some really cool demonstrations testing skin conductivity when someone lies. It was basically a lie detector test. There were wires, electrodes, screens, beeps, buzzers. It was totes amaze!!!

I looked into the course further online and found I could learn about the science behind exercise as well as how the body works when healthy and when diseased. The course would also teach me how exercise can be used as a treatment for illnesses too.

It was the perfect fit for me and gave me a backup plan if my idea to work for a premiership football team didn't pan out.

What happened next was unexpected and changed my life forever. You see, I fell completely in love with Physiology and everything to do with how the body works whilst studying the degree. During my time at university I worked in an exercise physiology lab, a biomedical science lab and learned so many new skills. While studying and working in these labs I learned all about the other areas of Biomedical Science such as Immunology and Microbiology, which in some of the different modules you can pick and choose from.

After 3 years at the University of Wolverhampton I completed my degree with a First (Hons). Not too shabby for someone who got a D at GCSE English and a C, a D and an E in

Chapter 1 – Why I Wrote This Book

Physics, Biology & Chemistry at A-level. (See page 43 as to what a First is).

So... what next?

Well, the University asked me to run their Exercise Science lab for several months, then offered me a job as a Physiology Demonstrator. In both roles I got to spend my time working with undergraduates on their 1st & 2nd year practical experiments, 3rd year projects, helping them by showing them how to use the equipment, how to write reports and guide them if they were stuck. This lead me to my second passion – teaching!

Eventually, I ended up working as a lecturer in Physiology at Birmingham City University teaching Nurses, Paramedics, Operating Department Practitioners and many other different careers. Whilst I was there I went on to study postgraduate Medical Toxicology at Cardiff University. Over the 5 years of lecturing, and meeting the students, I could see so many of them were about to follow their dream of working in the NHS.

That was my plan originally, to work in the NHS as a doctor. But my path was set to lecturing physiology... Or was it...

After 5 years of teaching at Birmingham City University I fancied a new challenge and decided to work for a new boss: that boss being me. The result of which was **MEDICAL MAVERICKS!** I knew there would be hundreds, if not thousands of pupils in schools across the UK who wanted to be Doctors, just like me. Many would never get the grades and would wander into some dull unrelated career like accountancy or end up in a call centre somewhere... Then there are the pupils that like science but don't ever consider a career in the NHS simply because they don't know what amazing jobs are out there, such as Physiology, Toxicology, and Biomedical Science, Medical Engineering, Ophthalmic Science. I could go on!

Chapter 1 – Why I Wrote This Book

And what about those students who don't think they are good enough. They might be predicted C/level 4 grades across the board at GCSE or be on the C-D/4-3 borderline.

Do any of these descriptions sound familiar? Is one of them you?

Working in the NHS is usually far from many students' minds, they think you have to some kind of Brainiac child genius, or they assume the NHS is made up of only Doctors and Nurses.

Well, they would be wrong and you would also be wrong if you think that. There are hundreds of careers to suit all academic abilities and backgrounds!

My mission was clear: Medical Mavericks would help students across the UK (and now the world!) discover careers in the NHS and healthcare professions they had never heard of... We would show them how many of the careers are far more accessible than a Doctor or Dentist. We would help give them access to the best opportunities in life and achieve amazing things with their careers.

This book is a brief guide to some of the careers in Healthcare Science, the area that my passions - Physiology, Toxicology and Biomedical Science - fall into. There's very little on Doctors, Nurses, Physiotherapists, Midwives or Dentists in this book, put me down if you were expecting that! All the careers are from Healthcare Science or the Allied Health Professions and have amazing prospects for those that work in them.

There is also no b***s*** in this book. Just real practical advice that can help you stand out from the crowd and give you the best chance of getting onto that course or into that career. There are no guarantees you will get there, but you need to give yourself the best shot possible and be true to yourself.

Chapter 1 – Why I Wrote This Book

Want to know more? ... Then read on. There are over 40 careers to consider in this book, but first you need to find out what Healthcare Science is all about!

Chapter 2

How to Use this Book

This book has been put together as an introduction to the world of Healthcare Science alongside several other special careers within the NHS. At the last count, there were at least 50 different careers spread over five different sectors in HCS, as well as something called the Allied Health professions. If you go to page 190 you can see some of the other sectors as I have put a brief guide to these in here too!

You can jump to individual careers in the Healthcare Science sectors by flicking through the book to look for certain career types that have been colour coordinated.

The career types are:

- **Physiology (Green)**
- **Life Sciences (Blue)**
- **Medical Physics & Engineering (Red)**
- **Allied Health (Purple)**
- **Other Awesome Careers (Orange)**

Within each section is a collection of specific careers. The titles are in the coloured band across the top of the page along with the salary range. There is a short description of what is involved in the career as well as a typical career path into that job, starting at your GCSEs.

Chapter 2 – How To Use This Book

The career path is not fixed, and what I mean by that is you can find other ways into the career. You don't have to necessarily follow the 'standard' route. I certainly didn't follow a typical route into Physiology or Toxicology.

This book also contains a section on key 'jargon' used throughout the book. Things like degree, post-graduate and how university degrees are graded. I mean, what the hell is a 2:1!? You can find this on page 43.

Chapters 10 and 11 also give some great advice on how to get your dream job, how to persevere and have a great mindset as well as how to improve your study techniques.

At the back of the book are even more resources that you can access online, from videos on YouTube to our very own App as well as where you can get A4 and A3 poster versions of the careers in this book.

So, where do you start?

Well, you can go through the whole book and see how many amazing careers there are or you can read the next chapter which introduces each of the 4 sections so you can get a flavour of what they are, before choosing one.

So, what are you waiting for…

NB

The information in this book was correct at the time of print. Sometimes the careers, job titles, courses and universities change and may not relate exactly to how they are described here. Please use this book as a starting point for inspiration and then use the suggested websites and phone numbers to find out more information.

Chapter 3

What the Hell is Healthcare Science?

Healthcare Science (HCS) is THE key career sector within the NHS. OK, OK, I know all careers in the NHS are important. If there were no Doctors or Nurses, patients would not be treated or cared for. But, if you look at this one major statistic, you'll see why HCS is so vital for the NHS:

85% of all diagnostic tests are carried out by Healthcare Scientists

I will say it again.... **EIGHTY FIVE PERCENT** of all diagnostic tests are carried out or assessed by Healthcare Scientists. That is a pretty awesome stat.

Even more incredibly, there are only 55,000 Healthcare Scientists in the whole NHS – that's only 5% of the entire NHS workforce!

5% of the NHS work force perform 85% of all diagnostic tests.

TOTALLY A.M.A.Z.I.N.G!!!

Chapter 3 – What The Hell Is Healthcare Science

Chances are that if you have ever had a blood test, or had a sample of some kind taken in a hospital like urine, cells and other less pleasant bodily fluids, had an X-ray or some kind of scan, somewhere along the way a HCS was involved. HCS aid Doctors in finding out what is wrong, so you can receive exactly the right treatment you need.

Then there are all the test samples taken by GPs and Nurses in the community at clinics. These have to be analysed and guess what, a HCS does this as well.

HCS is so vital for helping Doctors and other Medics diagnose but no one knows about them. This book aims to change that!

So, what types of career are there? There are careers that have patient contact every single day - where you get to work one on one with patients. There are careers where you are based in a lab and very rarely meet the people you are helping to treat. There are careers that are involved in surgery, careers that repair equipment, invent new equipment, give out radioactive medicine, take photographs, draw medical images, take part in organ transplants, store body tissues, store blood and much more.

These are the 4 different sectors in HCS:
- **Physiology**
- **Life Sciences**
- **Medical Physics and Medical Engineering**
- **Bio-informatics**

Take a look through and consider the careers in each section. Don't dismiss any of them just because you don't like the look of the title or think you can't do it. You may like lots of the careers and find it difficult to choose one, or you might not like any

Chapter 3 – What The Hell Is Healthcare Science

and that is also OK! You have at least eliminated Healthcare Science from the list of your future careers.

As a brief introduction, I have included my own opinion on each sector and the characteristics of who would enjoy working in them most. Can you spot any of these characteristics in yourself? Use the below as a basic guide, not all the careers in each sector will need all of the characteristics. Do check out the rest of the careers, you may surprise yourself!

Physiology

- Loves human biology
- Wants to work directly with people
- Likes carrying out experiments
- Has an interest in specific organs
- Is OK with blood (not all careers!)
- Excellent communicator and motivator
- Considerate

Life Science

- Has an interest in all things microscopic – bugs, germs, parasites & viruses
- Follows procedures & routines
- Likes working in a lab environment
- Can deal with working with bodily fluids and samples
- Is OK with blood
- Other interests might be genetics & cancers
- Likes using high tech kit

See next page for **Medical Physics, Engineering and Bioinformatics.**

Chapter 3 – What The Hell Is Healthcare Science

Medical Physics & Engineering

- Wants to build & invent things
- Has an interest in design, electronics and I.T
- Likes to figure out how things work – problem solver
- Is confident with maths & I.T
- Can be creative and imaginative
- Excellent communicator
- Likes coding & computers

Bioinformatics

- Would like to work in computing
- Interested in computer programming
- Can deal with statistics and maths
- Has some interest in biology, chemistry and physics
- Can be creative and imaginative
- Interested in genetics

The next four chapters look at each of these sectors in more detail. First up to the podium is **Physiology**!

Chapter 4

PHYSIOLOGY

My first love in science was Physiology.

Physiology is a bit like Human Biology. You get to learn about how the whole body works from the organ systems as a whole right down to the tiny chemical reactions and interactions that take place with a single cell.

However, in HCS you get to specialise!

What do you mean, "specialise"?

Well, you can focus on one particular part of the body that you think is awe-inspiring and you become a specialist in this area. For example, if you studied the heart (and the heart is pretty cool) you could become a Cardiac Physiologist. Study the lungs and you can become a Respiratory Physiologist. Here are the other types of Physiologist in HCS that are available, along with the organs they focus on. Pick your organ and you simultaneously pick your job!

Physiology Specialisms

- **Audiology** - the ears and hearing – see page 108.
- **Cardiac Scientist** - the cardiovascular system – see page 110.
- **Clinical Perfusion Science** - control blood flow in and out of the body during heart surgery – see page 112.

Chapter 4 – Physiology

- **Critical Care Science** – work with intensive care patients – see page 114.
- **Gastrointestinal Physiology** - the digestive system – see page 116.
- **Neurophysiology** - the brain and nerves – see page 118.
- **Ophthalmic & Vision Science** - the eyes – see page 120.
- **Respiratory & Sleep Physiology** - what happens when we sleep – see page 122
- **Urodynamic Science** - the kidneys, bladder and urinary system – see page 124
- **Vascular Science** - blood vessels – see page 126

Clearly there is a whole range of really cool careers in Physiology. Many, if not all of the above involve the HCS working directly with a patient to either test directly or take a sample for analysis. It's not just Doctors and Nurses that get to work with patients you know.

The type of patient you could work with varies a lot, this is also something you can specialise in. You could be working with all ages from little kiddies and wee babies through to OAPs. You may have seen a viral video of a baby having a hearing aid fitted for the first time and the delight on their face as they started to hear things. That would have been an Audiologist fitting the earpiece. It's not just grandparents that have them fitted. Go to **www.medicalmavericks.co.uk/book** to see the video of the baby!

Working one on one with a patient, means you will also see their frustrations first hand. I know from personal experience; my Dad had COPD (Chronic Obstructive Pulmonary Disease) that developed over many years, his frustration during the decline from a weight lifter and all round active person, to someone who was on oxygen 24/7 and could not walk more than 20 yards before having to stop.

These types of patients and many others will be part of your working life every day, so you need to be sympathetic, compassionate and have plenty of patience. You need to give encouragement and ensure that the patient understands that the tests you are putting them through will have an impact on their treatment and future health. This can be a tough job but oh so rewarding.

To find out more about these careers, see the **GREEN** section.

BONUS RESOURCES

You can check out the baby having the hearing aid fitted by going to **www.medicalmavericks.co.uk/book**

Chapter 5

LIFE SCIENCES

These guys and girls are what you would traditionally call a "classic scientist", with some of them wearing a white lab coat, gloves and safety specs, as their main area of work is in a lab. Any samples that are taken typically end up with a Life Scientist for analysis. So, one Healthcare Scientist may actually pass on a sample to another Healthcare Scientist.

They really are like one big relay team!

Life Sciences are split up slightly differently to Physiology, there are three main areas with different careers in each one. Some careers actually cross over between these areas as well (just to confuse you). My personal favourite is Histocompatibility & Immunogenetics. If that isn't the best job title ever, I don't know what is! Go to page 146 to see what they do.

The three areas are:

- Pathology – diagnose, treat and monitor different diseases.
- Genetics – look at how genetics can cause and treat disease.
- Reproductive Science – research and treat infertility.

Chapter 5 – LIFE SCIENCE

Here are the careers that fit under each area.

Pathology

- **Analytical Toxicology** - drugs & poisons – see page 128.
- **Anatomical Pathology** – involved in post mortems – see page 130.
- **Biomedical Science** – lab tests to diagnose diseases – see page 132.
- **Blood Sciences** – studies blood diseases and involved in blood donation and transfusion – see page 134.
- **Cellular Sciences** – analyse cells from different tissues.
- **Clinical Biochemistry** – analyse bodily fluids – see page 136
- **Clinical Immunology** – looks at conditions of the immune system – see page 138.
- **Cytopathology and Cervical Cytology** – looks at cellular diseases and smear tests – see page 140.
- **Haematology** – looks at blood conditions and how blood is formed in conditions like leukaemia – see page 144.
- **Histopathology** – prepares and examines tissue samples – see page 144.
- **Microbiology** – looks at bacteria, viruses, fungal and parasitic infections – see page 148.
- **Phlebotomy** – takes blood samples.
- **Virology** – studies infections caused by viruses – see page 152.

Chapter 5 – LIFE SCIENCES

Genetics

- **Genetics** – looks at patient's DNA to identify diseases – see page 142.
- **Histocompatability & Immunogenetics** – matches organ donors to organ recipients – see page 146.

Reproductive Science

- **Reproductive Science and Andrology** – treats and studies reproductive diseases and works in IVF – See page 150

You could call these peeps the engine room of the HCS as they pretty much handle ALL lab tests in some way or another. The one key point here is, you <u>have</u> to be OK with handling other people's bodily fluids and samples. This could include anything from sputum (spit or phlegm), urine, poo, blood, semen, puss, brain fluid or any other secretion that can come from the body.

There is the potential you could also be dealing with some very serious conditions as well. Imagine having to work with a couple that are struggling to have a baby and you are guiding them through IVF. Or what about completing a test that diagnoses someone with HIV. Or analysing a test that confirms leukaemia in a 3-year-old girl. These are all totally life changing results that you have to handle and deliver.

All the tests and results could have an emotional impact on you if you don't learn to distance yourself from the result. This can be quite tough at first, but over time you will learn how to control your emotions and not become emotionally involved. This doesn't make you heartless, it's something you will need to do to complete your job to the best ability you can.

BONUS RESOURCES

Check out **www.medicalmavericks.co.uk/book** where you can see how I had to produce my own sputum sample.

Chapter 6

MEDICAL PHYSICS & ENGINEERING

Medical Physics and Engineering is a kind of "kill two birds with one stone" set of careers, which can make things a little confusing for you guys. Plus, some of the careers actually mix physics and engineering in the same job role (to make it extra difficult). There are some very special careers in here that make a major impact on people's lives. You could be re-building someone's face after a burns injury, creating images and scans from MRI & Ultrasound machines or just making sure equipment is working correctly across the hospital (a massively important and hugely understated job). There is even a career for those with a creative side.

Let's take a look at the full list.

- Clinical Measurement & Development
- Clinical Pharmaceutical Science
- Imaging (Non-Ionising)
- Medical Device Risk Management & Governance
- Medical Illustration & Clinical Photography

Continued on next page….

Chapter 6 – MEDICAL PHYSICS & ENGINEERING

- Nuclear Medicine
- Reconstructive Science
- Radiotherapy Physics
- Rehabilitation Engineering
- Renal Technology

A key skill needed to work in these departments is team work. You definitely need to be a 'people person' as you will be working closely with all members of staff at the hospital, not just Healthcare Scientists. Patient contact is also part of the job, and not just in hospitals, you could be out in the community as well. Communication is key as repairing or maintaining pieces of kit is critical for the health of patients, one misunderstanding could be disastrous. Imagine not repairing the kit correctly and it is needed in an emergency! That could be the difference between life and death for a patient.

Maths is also a biggy here. It is important across all areas of HCS and the NHS, but more so here especially when dealing with radiation and medications. You don't want to overdose or over expose a patient or fellow colleagues to too much radiation! It is definitely not like in the movies... you won't be getting any super powers...there are no radioactive spiders in the NHS... More likely they will die from too much radiation!

It's not just about maths, physics and building things either, oh no. If you are creative and have an 'Arty' side there is a HCS career to check out. Believe it or not hospitals actually need illustrators and photographers! A Clinical Photographer may be involved in before and after images of a patient going through reconstructive treatments, or an illustrator may have to create images for a publication. There are also careers for musicians & drama teachers too! Check out page 194 to see where these come in to the NHS.

After this brief introduction you can see there is quite a broad range of careers in this sector.

BONUS RESOURCES

Check out **www.medicalmavericks.co.uk/book** to see a Clinical Photographer in action and find out how they got into this career!

Chapter 7

BIOINFORMATICS

Bioinformatics is one the newest & fastest growing areas of not just HCS, but the NHS as a whole. Why? Well, technology has developed in leaps and bounds in the last few years so we can now start to use I.T and computing to help improve the efficiency of the NHS, make faster decisions about patient care and provide better treatments.

Let me explain...

There are three areas of **Bioinformatics**:

- **Genomics**
- **Health Informatics**
- **Physical Sciences**

Each uses I.T in a different way to improve patient care. Think of it like this: bioinformatics is connecting computer science to biology to information science to medicine. It is the 'I.T string' that connects and holds everything together.

Genomics

You have probably seen some futuristic film where all our data is stored in a bar code or on a digital file somewhere. Well that future is here! Projects like the Human Genome Project have led to medical institutions being able to store an individual's biological data

Chapter 7 – BIOINFORMATICS

on a computer. In years to come your whole genetic code could be stored as a digital file and be analysed to find the best treatment or even discover your susceptibility to a disease. In fact, you can now look at your genetics to work out how responsive you would be to breast cancer treatments. This is called precision medicine.

It's not just genetic code that can be stored digitally. X-Rays, MRI scans, patient notes, test results and more are now all being stored digitally. Not only does this reduce the space required for storing paper records, it can speed up how quickly a medic can access or see a patient file.

Health Informatics

This one does what it says on the tin – they provide information on health! Part of the role is involved in connecting and collecting data from biological processes and tests. They make sure readings and data are collected in a secure and standardized way before analysing the results. Health Informatics personnel work with senior members of hospital management to provide analysis and explanation of data so they can make strategic decisions about the hospital. They also work with patients or create literature that explains results in a way that patients can understand.

Physical Sciences

Physical Sciences is a little different from the previous two we have just looked at. Instead of doing the collecting and lots of analysis, you could be designing the software, programmes and interfaces that data is collected on, making it easier to do and easier to collect analytics. You may also be involved in writing software that models biological processes. An example of which would be modelling how a drug is metabolised by the liver and how it affects the body. This kind of programming is used in Patient Simulators that medics train on.

Chapter 7 – BIOINFORMATICS

They can give a drug electronically to a 'dummy' and the medical observations like heart rate, respiration rate and blood pressure change as a result of the drug being given in real time. These changes are part of the 'model' that was programmed in Bioinformatics.

Coding is one of the biggest growth areas at the time of writing. Think about your mobile phone and your Fitbit. These pieces of technology can monitor your heart beat, the number of steps you take and so much more and it all needs coding.

Just imagine what the future holds. An ultrasound in your pocket? Scans that diagnose you in seconds? Or how does a virtual Doctor sound? Just type your symptoms into a computer and artificial intelligence gives a diagnosis! It is all coming down the tracks!

Chapter 8

THE BEST BIT

This is the best bit in the whole book. Seriously, it is!

Why?

Because I am about to tell you what YOU need to do at school to work in any of the careers showcased in this book.

Are you ready?.....Drum roll please.......

DDDDDDRRRRRRRRRRRRR (that's a drum roll btw!)

To take the first step into a Healthcare Science career you need to get 9-4/A-C grades in Maths, English & Science.

Sound ridiculous, I know. Everyone reading this book should manage to do that!! But if you can get grades 9-4/A-C in Maths, English and Science you can find a route into Healthcare Science. Many other medical based professions need 8-9/A & A* grades, but not HCS. Getting those pass grades in those three subjects is the essential part of getting into Healthcare Science, making them super accessible to many levels of ability.

Accessing all these awesome jobs with lower grades does not detract from these careers in any way. They are still well paid, challenging and very important roles in the NHS with lots of opportunities.

Chapter 8 – THE BEST BIT

Remember: they do 85% of the diagnostic tests! Just because you don't need the A & A* grades doesn't mean it is an easy job. Oh no, far from it. You still have to know your stuff and go through training and different courses to qualify. But the start point is those 9-4/A-C grades in Maths, English and Science, putting them easily within your reach!

My own experience is a great example of how to get into Healthcare Science. At GCSE I got A grades in Science, a B in Maths and a D (yes a D!) in English. That D grade let me down, but my school was great and they let me re-sit English whilst in Sixth form and I came out with a B.

My Sixth form A-Level grades were nothing to shout about either. I got a C, D and an E in Physics, Biology and Chemistry respectively. Not exactly setting the world alight with those grades, and certainly not the A/A* everyone thinks you need to work in the NHS.

Important piece of advice here: if you don't get those grades the first time round, **do not** give up! Go back and try again. It may take longer, but who cares? Reading this, your life expectancy living in the UK is 81.6 years, what's an extra year or two in that context? If you have a dream you have to work for it. My own Dad went back to do his GCSEs (or O-levels as they were then called) in his late 30s and didn't finish University until he was 45!

Once you've achieved those grades, what next? You have your GCSEs, where do you go now?

This bit is up to you. You have to do a little bit of research and do the work pretty much 99% of your friends and colleagues at school will not do. Set yourself apart from everybody else.

Follow the next section on setting your goals. Write them down and then do the research to find out exactly what you need to achieve to get there. Look on University websites, UCAS, the NHS Health Careers website to find out all you can about the course and what is required to get yourself a coveted place as a university student!

If Uni isn't for you, then fear not! There are other routes in through apprenticeships and degree apprenticeships where you learn on the job and get qualified at the same time.

For hints and tips on how to stand out from the crowd, see chapter 11. The careers in this book also all have a rough guide to what is required. Check them out from page 108.

BONUS RESOURCES

The number and types of apprenticeships that are available change all the time. To find the latest information on these qualifications visit the NHS Careers website:

www.healthcareers.nhs.uk

Chapter 9

JARGON & LINGO

Throughout this book and in your school life, you may hear different words being used about careers, university, routes to employment, qualifications and courses you can study on, and you may not want to admit you don't have a CLUE about what they mean... This is a brief guide to some of these words and terms, we will start with the classic route, before looking at alternatives.

Let's start at the beginning.

When you are at school, you can study your GCSEs (General Certificate of Secondary Education) in years 10 & 11. In 6th form or college you can study your A-Levels, BTECs (Business and Technology Education Council), IBACs (International Baccalaureate) and then after that where do you go? We are going to focus on the University route here, but at the end of the chapter there is more info on other routes after GCSE and Sixth Form, including Apprenticeships.

A Degree

A degree is a course you study at University. You can choose your subject by looking through a University prospectus or searching the UCAS website. Typically, a degree is three years long.

Chapter 9 – JARGON & LINGO

However, some courses are 4 years as they include a placement year where you leave the course to work in a sector linked to your degree, or work abroad, for a year. You can also study part time, but the courses take 5-6 years to complete. There are several types of degree available, we will go through each one on the following pages.

Undergraduate Degree

This is the first degree you can take at university after Sixth form or college. Typically, you study different modules and topics over the three (or four) years. You are assessed at your University by taking exams, writing essays and performing presentations. In your 3rd year of your degree you can complete a major project called an Honours Project (see below) as well as a Dissertation, which is pretty much a 10,000 word essay!

BSc (Hons) or Bachelor of Science (Hons)

There are different types or titles of degree you can take. This is not the subject! For example, a degree subject could be Human Biology or History. The type of degree is usually listed on the University website and UCAS. A science based degree has the title BSc, which stands for Bachelor of Science. Other degree titles examples include:

- **BA – Bachelor of Arts.**
- **BEd – Bachelor of Education**
- **BEng – Bachelor of Engineering**

Chapter 9 – JARGON & LINGO

A degree with Hons...

Hons refers to 'Honours'. For example, my degree was: BSc (Hons) in Human Physiology & Exercise Science. You get the Hons bit by completing a project in your 3rd year called, guess what... an honours project!

In Science, this usually includes you having to come up with your own experiments and theory to test in a lab. My honours project tested professional footballers and the heart rates they trained at, as well as linking it to how much lactic acid they produced during training. Some of my friends did projects on how bone was destroyed by increases in temperature when it was drilled during certain types of surgery, how caffeine affected performance in explosive and endurance sports, and how exercise affected your immune system. All cool stuff, but really hard work.

When you complete your degree, you become a Graduate.

WOOHOOO WELL DONE YAYYYY!!!!

The Degree Results

- **First** – Also known as a Geoff Hurst (if you don't know who Geoff Hurst is, then shame on you!).
  This is the top result you can get. Around 20% of graduates get a First. Think of it like an A grade and you usually have to have an average pass grade of 70% or more.
- **2:1 – Or Upper Class Degree.**
  This is the next grade down. Almost like a B grade and you have to average 60-69% in your assessments. Around 45% of graduates get a 2:1.
- **2:2 – AKA a 'Desmond'**... why? For some strange reason it was linked to Archbishop Desmond Tutu... get it 2:2...
  This is like a C grade and requires an average of 50-59% in assessments. It can also be known as a Lower Second Class Degree.

- **3rd** – The lowest official grade you can get. It is awarded if your average results in assessments are in the 40-49% range.
- **Unclassified** - This is a pass and to be honest it is worth less than the paper it's written on, as you have only averaged around the 40% mark in assessments, or potentially below. That may sound harsh, but if you don't do the work, the university is not just going to hand out results on a platter. **Avoid at all costs.**

Postgraduate Degree

Once you have completed your undergraduate degree, if you liked it so much you can go on to study at an even higher level on a Postgraduate Course of which there are several types. The order of which are:

- **Post Graduate Certificate**
- **Post Graduate Diploma**
- **Masters**

One usually leads into another, or you can go straight into the Masters. When I studied my post-grad course in Medical Toxicology, you started off studying for the certificate, if you passed certain modules you qualified for the Diploma and then if you wanted to, at the end of that, you could study for another year for the Masters. The whole process for the above takes between 1 – 2 years and varies at different Universities.

PhD

PhD stands for Doctorate in Philosophy. It is a research based qualification with no lectures or classic teaching lessons. At the end of it you can call yourself a doctor!

Chapter 9 – JARGON & LINGO

You're not a medical doctor. You are a doctor in your subject. You can become a doctor in any subject: languages, history, art, science, medicine…the list could go on. Some people put the letters PhD at the end of their name, some put Dr at the start. So, don't assume when you see someone with Dr at the start that they are a medical doctor!

Check out one of our favourite PhD / Dr memes on our website **www.medicalmavericks.co.uk/book**

Typically, you can start a PhD once you have a Masters. You don't always need a Masters, but many students use it as a stepping stone to a PhD.

You get a PhD after extensively researching an original idea or concept in your chosen subject. It usually takes 4-8 years to complete as you are finding out something no one has ever found out before in a subject and this takes time. There are so many facets to science subjects, there is always something to discover.

In a science based PhD you'll spend a lot of time in the lab performing experiments, analysing results, writing reports and papers that get published in scientific journals. These are critiqued by other scientists to make sure the science stands up! It can be quite brutal… but you can't have duff science. Your results and findings could go on to change the world!

After your PhD, you can carry on researching in what is called a Post Doc (post doctorate). You may even become a Professor!

Many PhD graduates go on to become an academic. This is where you are the expert in your field at the University and you teach about it as a lecturer in University. However, you don't always need a PhD to become a lecturer. I became a lecturer at the age of 24 with just a degree!

But what if you go down another route? - There are other types of degree.

Chapter 9 – JARGON & LINGO

There are several other types of degree that sit academically under a normal undergraduate degree, but above A-levels. Think of these as alternatives or stepping-stones towards an undergraduate degree that depend on the type of course you are studying and for how long.

The qualifications include Higher National Certificate (HNC), Foundation Degree, Certificate in Higher Education, Diploma in Higher Education and Higher National Diploma (HND).

You can do these in standard degree subjects that do not have a work related or vocational element to them, for example Biology.

After 1 year of University study you can be awarded a **Certificate of Higher Education** (CertHE). Some courses offer this straight up but you can also be awarded it if you complete and pass your 1st year of university and decide to drop out or stop.

After 2 years of university study you can be awarded a **Diploma in Higher Education** (DipHE). This qualification is common in many medical or health based careers such as Nursing, Operating Department Practitioners and Paramedic Science. Yes, I know I said these qualifications don't normally have a work-related element… But I don't make the rules! Qualifications like Nursing and Paramedics Science may also take 3 years as well as opposed to the normal 2.

Courses that have a work related or vocational element are known as a Higher National Certificate (HNC), Foundation Degree, and **Higher National Diploma** (HND).

The Higher National Certificate is a qualification that is equivalent to 1 year of a full University course. It can be offered as a stand-alone qualification, or if you complete your 1st year of a normal degree but then decide to pull out.

Chapter 9 – JARGON & LINGO

A Higher National Diploma and Foundation Degree are both 2 year courses and are the equivalent to completing two years of a standard 3 year honours degree. They sit one level below a full degree and can usually be topped up to a full degree by studying for a third and final year.

Sometimes if you don't get the grades you need or you haven't quite got the right qualifications, universities let you do a Foundation Degree before you enrol on the course of your choice.

There is some work place learning and many companies actually fund their employees to complete this type of degree if they have not already studied to this level. The NHS is very good at this.

Healthcare Science Course Jargon

Many of the careers in this book will require you to follow a specific path to get to it. Some of these paths will require you to go on either a Practitioner Training Programme or a Scientist Training Programme. This is what they both mean.

Practitioner Training Programme (PTP)

The PTP is a specific degree that can take you directly into a healthcare science career. Basically, it is an NHS approved and accredited undergraduate BSc honours degree in healthcare science. This means you can study on these courses as soon as you have completed your A-levels or BTECs (Sixth form / college qualifications). You can find these degrees by searching UCAS for healthcare science. However, that is not all! These degrees have themes and specialisms, of which there are five:

- **Cardiovascular, respiratory & sleep sciences**
- **Neurosensory sciences**
- **Pathology sciences**

Chapter 9 – JARGON & LINGO

- Medical physics
- Clinical Engineering

Each of the above contain different specialisms that you will study throughout the course. Over the three years you complete a total of 50 weeks workplace learning & training placements – that's roughly half your time at university, it's not all about studying in a lecture theatre!

You also get to choose what you specialise in over the final 2 years. For example, if you were studying for a neurosensory degree, you could specialise in any of the following: audiology, neurophysiology, ophthalmic and vision science. You would try all of these in the first year and then specialise over the next two in the area you find especially interesting.

At the end of the degree, you will be suitably trained and qualified to apply for positions as a healthcare scientist in the area of specialism that you have studied. However, there is no guaranteed job at the end of the course. You need to do all of the CV things we mention in Chapter 11 to make yourself stand out to get that awesome job you really want.

Scientific Training Programme (STP)

The STP is slightly different to the PTP. With STP you have to already have a degree of some kind related to science or health such as Biology or Biochemistry. The result of your degree should be a 1st or a 2:1, but 2:2s are sometimes considered if you have other postgraduate degrees as well. STP is known as a graduate entry programme, as you have to be a graduate to apply.

Another difference is that you are employed by an NHS trust to complete the STP and become a healthcare scientist for

Chapter 9 – JARGON & LINGO

them when you complete your training. This means you are paid to train! How awesome is that!

It is still a three-year course, but you are mainly based in a workplace training on the job. You can still try out lots of different areas and then specialise during 2nd and 3rd year resulting in a master's degree at the very end.

Just like the PTP the STP has its own specialisms and themed courses.

These are:

- Microbiology
- Blood sciences
- Cellular sciences
- Genetic sciences
- Neurosensory sciences
- Cardiovascular, respiratory and sleep sciences
- Gastrointestinal physiology and urodynamic sciences
- Clinical Engineering
- Medical physics
- Informatics

There are loads of sub specialisms within these and you will read about them in the careers section.

This could be the perfect route if you are not sure what you want to do yet, but know you love science, health and medical topics. I took this route. I studied Human Physiology & Exercise Science, before studying for a post-graduate degree in Medical Toxicology. Making a decision on what you want to do as a career is a big choice, this can be a great way to get into an area you like and are interested in without committing to anything too early.

Bear in mind, there is only one round of applications per year for the STP. The number of posts and locations of these also vary year to year. In 2016 there were 258 STP posts available to apply for across the whole of England and Wales, but 5,768 applicants. You need to be on it with your CV and application to make sure you are one of those few!

To find out more about these posts and when to apply just go to www.healthcareers.nhs.uk and search for STP in the search bar on that webpage.

Apprenticeships

These are in the news and talked about in education all the time at the moment. If you've not heard of an apprenticeship before, it is basically a way to learn on the job. You get paid and get a qualification at the end! So, it is the perfect choice if you want a more hands on role, rather than a more formal education route.

At the time of writing, you can take apprenticeships in:

- **Leadership & Management**
- **Allied Health Profession Support**
- **Clinical Healthcare Support**
- **Dental Nursing**
- **Emergency Care Assistance**
- **Informatics**
- **Maternity & Paediatric Support**
- **Perioperative Support**
- **Pharmacy Services**
- **Health & Social Care**
- **Healthcare Science Assistant**
- **Healthcare Science Associate**
- **Nursing degree apprenticeships**

Chapter 9 – JARGON & LINGO

That last one might sound a little different but there are such things as degree apprenticeships. Yep, that's right! You can do an apprenticeship and come out with a degree at the end of it! You get the best of both worlds. Lots of hands on experience, a salary and a degree at the end of it!

The best place to look for apprenticeships is on the NHS jobs website. This is where they all get listed, no matter where you are in the UK. The web address is www.jobs.nhs.uk

One other top tip is to contact your regional NHS trust and ask them which apprenticeships are available or when they are starting. To do this, hop over to Google and search for your region / county and the words 'NHS Trust'.

Chapter 10

HOW TO GET TO YOUR DREAM

Listen up, there is something categorically important I need to tell you alongside what you need to do in school, and that thing is this….

You need a plan. A plan or route map from where you are now to where you want to go and who you want to be. This is a big **BIG** question for anyone, let alone a teenager!

But… if you can visualize and write it all down and make it real you will have more chance of achieving your goal. There is lots of evidence to back this up as well (I'm not just telling you mumbo-jumbo)!

A study many years ago followed students from Harvard University in America (one of the top Universities in the world!). In the study, they asked students if they had any goals in business and in life. The results were as follows:

- 84% had no specific goals.
- 13% had goals but had not written them down.
- 3% had clear, written goals and plans to accomplish them.

Ten years later, these students were interviewed again and one of the biggest findings was that the 3% who had written their goals down, earned ten times as much money as the other 97% of students that were interviewed.

This is staggering! OK, yes, they were looking at wealth. But you can be certain that those who had written down their goals had written down something about how much they wanted to earn.

You can do the same too and it definitely doesn't have to be a monetary goal. It can be a goal about what job you would like, where you would like to live, what kind of person you would like to be. It is all linked, but without committing it to paper and having a plan, the chances of achieving the goal are very, very slim.

Let's get planning, where do you start and what do you do? Start where you are now, what are your predicted grades, what did you get? Then, write down the end goal and a date. For example, it might be something like this:

By September 2020 I want to have completed my degree in Healthcare Science and started my position as a Biomedical Scientist.

Don't worry if it takes you some time to get this statement just right. You might not know the course you need to study yet, but know the job you want. If that is the case, use that instead. The key thing is to include a date and specific outcome.

Put this statement somewhere that you will see it every single day, ideally at the start of the day when you first wake up. Somewhere like next to the bathroom mirror, on your bedside table, in your notebook, as your desktop picture on your computer or your wallpaper of your phone.

Be proud of it! Don't hide it! Sure, some people will look at you oddly, but they don't have a plan and probably have some crappy job they hate. You are different, you know what you want and are going to get it!

Remember, your brain believes what you tell it. If you put a plan and set of goals in front of you every day, it is at the forefront of your mind all the time. However, your subconscious brain starts formulating plans and looking for ideas and opportunities that will help achieve them. Sounds weird I know, part of your brain doing stuff you're not controlling, but believe me, it happens and it works.

When you have your goal written down, the next part is to identify the gap between where you are now and what you want to achieve. This gap is anything and everything from the courses you have to go on, the grades you need to achieve, the applications you have to do, the work experience you can go on and things you can do make yourself stand out from the crowd. These are the stepping-stones to your end goal. You might not know them all at the start and it might seem overwhelming, but you can make a rough start and fill in more steps as you find out more. It's important to focus on what you can do now, this week, this month, to get to each of those stepping stones.

This is where you need to do a little research and keep a constant eye out for opportunities. Look at the different degrees you can study, the courses and careers. What do they specifically need you to do? Find out and put it in your plan! Entry grades for Universities can change each year so make sure you recheck at a later date to ensure your plan is up-to-date. Think about work experience, life experience, volunteering, clubs, organisations, teams you can join. It all strengthens your applications to Uni or courses you want to go on. Put them in your plan!

This doesn't end with your education either. You need to embrace this whole philosophy with your whole life as well. How do you spend your spare time? Do you waste hours on Facebook looking at statuses of people you know but have not met in person, and probably won't, for years and years? Do you listen to or watch the news? Do you listen to music whilst travelling? Think about all your actions in your life and how they are helping you achieve your ultimate goal. 90% of what you do in your life probably doesn't.

Admittedly, not all of it should, don't get me wrong we all need some down time! I love going out, having fun, spending time with friends, but when it comes to it if you really want to achieve your goal you have to make some sacrifices.

It's about doing things today that others won't, so you can live your life the way that others can't.

That last statement is so important, I will say it again!

It's about doing things today that others won't, so you can live your life the way that others can't.

Sounds daunting, boring and dull, but it isn't. For example, I do three or four really simple things every day that improves the chances of me meeting my goals. Yes, I have goals too, even at 37.... You should never stop this process by the way. It will serve you well your entire life!

For example:

- **Listen to audiobooks**

I listen to audiobooks and podcasts whilst driving or going for a run, on topics and subjects that are linked to my goal and that I enjoy and find interesting. As an entrepreneur, that means I listen to business & motivational books. Check out the App Audible on your tablet or smart phone. You can download a book a month for a few quid or buy them out right and have a whole library on your phone. Check out the iTunes Podcast section. There are tons of different categories of podcasts and thousands of podcasters pumping out information for you to download and listen to!

Chapter 10 – HOW TO GET TO YOUR DREAM

- **Read more!**

Again, using your phone or tablet, download the Kindle App. E-books are cheap as chips and you can always find books that can help you for very little money at all. If you are a paper books person through and through, university town book stores are a great place to pick up second hand books that will be relevant to your subject. Read or listen to your books whilst travelling around in the car or on the bus. Use that time wisely!

- **Plan your days**

On an afternoon or evening, write your to do list or plan for the next day. No more than 5-7 tasks are needed. That way when you get up, you are not wasting time thinking what have I got to do today? It is already there for you to get up and get on with. Put them in order of priority, usually start with the toughest task of them all. Humans like to avoid the difficult so get it done and out of the way first thing. All the other tasks will be easy!

- **Time block your day.**

What I mean by this is work for 45, 60 or 90 minutes solid on your tasks, whatever time length works for you. Then take a break for 10-15 minutes. DO NOT GO ONTO FACEBOOK! Step away from your desk, computer or where ever you are working and make a drink, play with the dog, do some press ups, read, colour, anything other than sitting at your desk. (BTW I will admit to being a total Facebook addict and have to slap myself round the face to stop me from logging in just for a quick status update!).

Chapter 10 – HOW TO GET TO YOUR DREAM

Check out chapter 14 for more on passing your exams in 90 Minutes.

- ### Get up 30 minutes earlier than normal

Start work 30 minutes before you used to or before anyone else you know does. Do that 5 days a week and you have gained 2.5 hours of extra time each week to get to your goal. Especially relevant to revision! Over 52 weeks, you have just gained 5.4 days' worth of time. What would you do with an extra 5 days?

- ### This is a biggy for me: silence is golden.

On two counts: Firstly, be comfortable with your own thoughts. Your brain has so much thrown at it each day with videos, music, emails, lessons, phone calls, texts and messages that you hardly have time to process any thoughts of your own. Take time out each day to have no distractions whether that is on a walk to school, riding a bike or just sitting quietly in your room… almost meditating to take you away from distractions and hear your own thoughts. This might sound a bit woo-woo and a bit airy-fairy, but seriously think about when was the last time you didn't have a phone or computer more than 5 feet away from you pinging or drawing you in to check a Tweet or Facebook or Instagram or Snapchat status update.

Personally, I like to go running **WITHOUT HEADPHONES** and just think about other stuff whilst running. If I have a problem I want to solve or something is bugging me a run or bike ride with normally figure it out. Sometimes I don't think about anything at all, I just admire the scenery.

Chapter 10 – HOW TO GET TO YOUR DREAM

Take the time to turn off your devices, listen to yourself and you will feel far better for it. This goes for bed time too. The light from your phone in the dark messes with your brain and makes it think it is day time so you can't sleep very well. Try it for a few days. No phone in the 1-2 hours before bed. I bet you sleep like a baby (that's a baby that sleeps through the night… not one that wakes screaming!).

Secondly, being able to work and concentrate in silence can play a massive part in your success. You can't listen to music in an exam, so why study with it on? Most people do this as some sort of distraction to make themselves feel better or make studying fun. 'It helps me concentrate!' they say, – That's just RUBBISH, RUBBISH, RUBBISH!!!

Don't get me wrong, this used to be me. I remember sitting down on the living room floor one afternoon to study for my A-levels. TV was on, but silent and a CD playing (that's how music USED to be played) at the same time. I remember thinking WTF am I doing! I'd spent about 30 minutes getting set up with my paper all over the floor, when I could just have gone to sit at my desk… in silence and got on with it, and done an extra 30 minutes of studying.

If this is you, I can pretty much predict what happens each time you sit down to study. You'll probably spend 5-10 minutes flicking through your track list choosing a song or album… you start to study….10 minutes later and a song you don't like comes on. 'Right' you say, 'I need to change that track' and off you go again distracted from your work.

Total utter madness.

If you think and act like this, you are coming at it from completely the wrong angle. Don't worry though, you are not alone!

The knowledge you are building from studying is taking you closer and closer, inch by inch, to your goals. Why impair that process? Plus, this knowledge is going to help you change and save lives. Now that is pretty awesome. Studying is like many things we put off or see as a chore. You take an age to start, but when you do, it is actually really satisfying and nowhere near as bad as you thought. In fact, after several periods like this, you'll wonder what all the fuss was about.

Now, there are many things that can influence your ability to achieve your goal. Life is a bastard sometimes and can throw some real curve balls at you to throw you off course. But if you have written it down, you now have a clear objective and everything you do from your studies to how you use your spare time, will take you one step closer to that dream.

Remember you get up each day with 1440 minutes to fill with 'stuff'.

How will you use each one of the minutes? Because once they are gone, they're gone!

Chapter 11

STANDING OUT FROM THE CROWD

When it comes to applying for jobs, getting onto courses or just being noticed there are several things you can do to make a real difference to your chances. This is especially important over the next 5-10 years. Why? Let me explain.

We are currently going through the early stages of the next 'industrial revolution'. But instead of iron and steel forges, it is the technological revolution. Pretty much everyone or every family in the western world has access to a smart phone, tablet, laptop or computer. These devices are used every moment of every day and are becoming an integral part of everyone's life. It is your generation that will be the first where your employers have also grown up with this technology and will have a greater understanding than previous generations.

What does this mean for you? Well, the way you apply for jobs may change, or to put it another way, you can change the way you apply for jobs and use the technology that is available to create a proposition to employ you that is so powerful you improve the chances of you getting the post by many, many times. The people you will be applying to will also be tech savvy, so you won't have to worry about if they understand what a mpeg or avi file is. They will engage with you more readily as you will be presenting them with an application that fits in with the way they lead their lives.

So here are my top tips!

Tip 1 – Don't do a boring CV!

I hate CVs. They are necessary in many circumstances but they can be so boring! Plus, who tells the truth in them anyway? Everyone embellishes in them to some degree, whether it's making you sound more qualified than you actually are or adding experiences that you have never really been through.

JUST STOP IT!

By all means have a nice standard CV prepared, but send it in with a memory stick or DVD/CD that has a 3-5 minute video all about you. This can take some practice, but it is one of the things that 99% of people will not do. Straight away you are different in the application process when a DVD drops out with your CV!

The video will show off who you really are, how well you can communicate, how innovative you are and it also shows you can use technology!

Now, before you say 'I haven't got a camera' or 'I don't know how to edit a video'. That is all rubbish! Chances are you have a smart phone with a decent camera or at least know someone that has. Use it or ask a friend to help you! It will do the job for this process. If you have a camcorder that is fab, but a decent smart phone camera will take good footage.

Editing is no problem either and it is simpler than you think. All Apple computers come with iMovie editing software and pretty much all Windows computers have Movie Maker. If you don't know how to use them, spend an evening on YouTube and search for *Movie Maker Tutorial* or *iMovie Tutorial* and look for the videos that cover the basics. There are loads of videos that will show you how to make a video.

What do you put in your video? You need to plan this a little, so create a storyboard. Get a piece of A4 paper and put it in landscape (longest edge across the top). Draw 6 boxes in two rows of three. Leave a little space underneath each one to write a note. In each box you can draw a little picture of what you want to film. You don't have to be Leonardo Di Vinci to do this. Stick people will do! It is just to give you an idea of what to talk about and what to film in what order.

BONUS RESOURCES

You can download a copy of a pre-prepared storyboard by visiting
www.medicalmavericks.co.uk/book

You can also see a video one of the members of Medical Mavericks did for their job application!

Remember to plan a start, middle and end of the video. For example, include an introduction describing who you are, what you are applying for and why you are doing the video (e.g. a video would be the perfect way to show you who I am and why I am suitable for the role). At the end, do a brief summary and include your contact details on the screen. They can pause the video to get these.

Be imaginative and draw inspiration from videos on YouTube, podcasts on your favourite subjects or even music videos. There is so much stuff out there, you are bound to be hit by a thunderbolt of inspiration. Film a talking head section where it is just you talking to the camera. Tell them about yourself, what you like doing, what your strengths and weaknesses are, what experience you have, but be sure do it in an imaginative way. Go to the sports club you belong to and be filmed taking part, film yourself at work, get a testimonial from your boss if you have a part time job, do something that is linked to the job you are applying for, tell them about your plans and goals!

Once you have filmed it all, put it together in the editing software and make sure it is around 3-5 minutes long. Remember to include your contact details within the video at the end.

Burn it to a DVD as well as a memory stick and send them both off with your CV. Use a brightly coloured envelope to make you stand out even more, basically anything but white or brown. Go for an A4 sized envelope if you can so you don't have to fold your CV. It may also be useful to put a piece of card into the envelope as well to protect the CD and memory stick.

If you are not sure where to get coloured or padded envelopes from, just search Google or even eBay. There are loads of companies that sell them (we use allcolourenvelopes.co.uk).

If you want to stand out even more, you can now buy video cards! That's right a card, just like a birthday card that has a small video screen inside. You can upload your own videos to them and even get them custom printed with your name, number and other details. How about that! You could have your CV written in the card and then have your video in there as well! That would be a killer application for any post! How much do they cost? You are looking at around £20-40 per card, so not cheap, but just think about the extra WOW factor when someone opens that envelope and is presented with a card that has your video playing inside!

Just search Google for **video card marketing or video card brochure** and several companies will come up that you can call to find out more.

Tip 2 – Get a website.

This sounds even more technical than making a video but trust me, it is really quite easy and cheap to do.

Chapter 11 – STANDING OUT FROM THE CROWD

The first thing to do is try and get a website address with your name in it. For example, I would look for something like:

www.tomwarrender.com or **www.tomwarrender.co.uk**

You can do this on websites like **www.123-reg.com** You can search for a web address, or domain as it is officially known, and then pay a few pounds to own it for so many years. You get a reminder when the renewal is due.

To get a website up and running check out **www.wordpress.org** . This is the best, easiest and quickest way to get a site up and running. If you are at school, go and see the school's IT department and ask them to help you out, they would love it! If you don't have this option, have a look around on YouTube for tutorials on how to set one up or do a Google search for a basic WordPress set up. You would have to pay for this but it would not be very much as you want a basic site. Think of it as an investment in your future!

Once it is up and running, set up your site as an online CV. Include your video on the home page along with a bio (overview about you!). You can add other pages including blogs about topics that interest you, video blogs or vlogs. Again use your imagination! It doesn't have to have hundreds of pages, just 3-5 basic pages that you can build on over time.

This is the killer bit… Imagine sending in your paper based CV and at the top of the page with all your contact info you have:

Check out my online CV: **www.tomwarrender.com**

How cool is that? How many other people have their own website. Not many. Along with the envelop, DVD and CV you are now way, WAY, **WAY** above anyone else who has applied. You could even put a page up on your site just for the job or course that you are applying for and include a link to that in the CV, For example:

www.tomwarrender.com/NHS-job-application

A lot of effort, but it will stand you in good stead over many years.

Tip 3 – Be aware of your Social Media presence.

I am sure you have a Twitter, Facebook, Instagram or Snapchat account and use it quite a lot. This is where you need to be careful. Pretty much any one can find you on these networks and find out what you have been up to or posting. Employers and course directors can quite easily search for you and find you within seconds to see your statuses.

You should always consider what you are posting, whether it is pictures, videos or written posts and comments. You may think a passing comment about how bad your day has been at work or how you don't like your boss or colleagues is all fine and gets you some sympathy from friends. But if a potential employer sees that, you may have just lost your chance for that job or course.

The key here is be yourself, but just be aware of what you are posting as it will be online forever and can be found by anyone!

Tip 4 is on the next page…

Chapter 11 – STANDING OUT FROM THE CROWD

Tip 4 – Go out of your way to learn & get experience.

The biggest problem for most people who want to work in health is getting work experience. The main reasons for this are numerous and include patient confidentiality, your safety, supervision and time. The main focus of a hospital is to provide care to their patients and bringing someone in on work experience could detract from this.

However, most people give up after writing one letter or getting their first rejection. This is where you can stand out. You can, of course, try to get some work experience, but another route to take is to try to interview as many people in the career of your choice and create a little portfolio of what you have discovered.

Think of it this way, you turn up for a university, job or apprenticeship interview and you get asked why do you want to go down this route, what do you know about the career, what do you think the toughest part of the job is, what do actually know about what goes on in the career? You can then say something like this:

"Well, I researched this career intensely by interviewing 5 different (INSERT CAREERS) over the past 6 months. I didn't like this other career after I found out X, Y & Z. But when I spoke to this other career I really liked what they had to say so I researched it some more and now I know I could do that job and it fits my ambitions.

I really liked the fact you get to work with patients every day and make decisions that will affect their recovery. The tests they perform really interest me. I know that some of the patients I will work with will have some very serious conditions and may not survive, so I know part of my role is going to provide more palliative care".

Chapter 11 – STANDING OUT FROM THE CROWD

And so on and so on... I hope you get the idea.

Please don't recite what I have written above in any of your interviews. The best thing to do is use your lips and ears in the proportions you have them... 1 mouth and 2 ears.... Ask the questions and then listen very carefully to what they have to say!

Now, imagine the response of the interviewer! The fact that you went out of your way to organise the interviews in your own time and have written your own portfolio about what you have found out and reflected on the information to make a decision with will totally blow them away!

You have shown them you have communication skills, you can think for yourself, you are pro-active, you know what career you want and have made a very informed decision about what you want to do. You have shown that you know what the career entails and have eliminated other career possibilities. You are pretty much an ideal candidate!

How do you go about organising the interviews? This is the slightly tricky part, but it is not as tricky as trying to get work experience... although at the end of your interview you can always be cheeky and ask if it is possible to come in for a half day, a day or even a few days!

Tip 5 - It's not always what you know, it's who you know.

Do you know any one at all that works in a hospital or the NHS in general? It could be a secretary, a receptionist or even a surgeon. People know people and you can always ask for their help!

For example, I wanted to have some pictures taken of me in a clinical setting. My Mom works as a receptionist in an Outpatients Department, so I asked her if she could ask one of the

68

lead nurses in the department if I could use a clinical room either at the start of the day or at the end of the day when it was not in use.

Guess what... they said yes.

Do you know someone that is receiving treatment in hospital or has to visit regularly? Could you ask them to find out who the best person is to talk to? Or could you even go to the hospital with them or visit them and do some research whilst on site?!

Don't be afraid to ask.... The worst that can happen is that they say no.

Always remember to have a note pad and pen on you in these circumstances. I'm sure you've got a good memory, but when someone does say yes, you need to take down their name, email, phone number, best time to call, where they work and so on. You don't want to be scratting around for a piece of scrap paper that can then be easily lost.

You can use your phone as well to take notes. Have a look through your apps to see if you have a notes app. If not, check out an app called Evernote. It's one big online note taking system and I couldn't live without it now... In fact, parts of this book have been written whilst on the move in Evernote.

Tip 6 - Do some research & be inventive!

If there is a particular department you want to reach, for example haematology, go on your local hospital's website and search for haematology. You may find a name of a person who works in that department that you can call (see next tip!). You may even discover the head of department or even their secretary.

Chapter 11 – STANDING OUT FROM THE CROWD

Another trick is search Google for words like 'Head of Department – Haematology *YOUR HOSPITAL / TOWN*. You never know what will come up.

Check out Linked In too. They have a pretty good search section where you can find people with specific job titles in different regions of the UK (Linked In is like the business version of Facebook. Not so much entertainment, more of a professional space you can promote yourself and find jobs and meet like-minded people).

Tip 7 - Pick up the phone.

Most people hate this bit. For some reason calling someone you don't know is a really difficult thing to do. The key is to be prepared and have a script written with all the things you want to ask and say so you don't sound like a mumbling fool with lots of eeeerrrrsss and pauses.

Take 30-40 minutes to write down what you want to say. You'll only have to do this once and then re-jig after a call if what you said didn't work or you pick up on something the person on the other end of the phone says about your call.

What do you put in your script? Well, it's quite simple really…

- Thank them for taking your call (yes, this is at the start!!)
- Tell them who you are
- Tell them you are really interested in this area as a career
- You know work experience is difficult to come by
- So, you would like to interview someone in that area to find out more about it
- It could be the person you are speaking to, or someone else in the department

Chapter 11 – STANDING OUT FROM THE CROWD

- The interview will take 20-30 minutes and you are happy to visit before, during or after their working day and not disrupt them too much
- Do you think that this would be possible?
- If not, do you know anyone else or anywhere else I could go to interview someone in and around this sector?
- If they can, tell them if you're under 18 and an adult will be with you and if this is OK?

Obviously be polite and say thank you for taking your call. These guys and girls are busy people and are involved in saving lives.

Be as accommodating as you can to fit in with their schedule – (Teachers, if you are reading this next bit.... I'm sorry!). They may only be able to see you whilst you're at school. Ask your parents if they are OK with you missing school to do the interview before your start this whole process! Get them to read this book, or this section, so your parents can understand what you are trying to do. I am sure they will be supportive! This means that if the scientist says they can only see you on a Tuesday afternoon, you can agree straight away.

Don't go missing exams or anything like that. Missing a lesson or an afternoon of school is a big deal, so your school probably won't like it. However, if you are missing a couple of lessons to go and interview someone that can help you make one the most important decisions of your life, I think that is a fair trade. You can obviously, try to organise the interviews for holiday times as well.

Don't cancel your meeting and don't be late either. These people have gone out their way to help you - DON'T MESS THEM AROUND!

Chapter 11 – STANDING OUT FROM THE CROWD

Once you have had your interview, send them a thank you card in the post. You could email them, but that is too easy. Writing a thank you card shows you have taken the time to sit down and write a personal message to the person that has helped.

Tip 8 - BE CHEEKY!

If you are really struggling to find the right person via phone or email, write a couple of letters and actually go and visit your hospital. Have a wonder round to try to see if you can find any signs for the department you are looking for. If you can't see or find it, ask someone! Go to a receptionist, stop someone in the corridor, just ask. They will more than likely give you directions.

Once in and around the area you want to be in, stop someone that is walking in and out of the department and explain what you are trying to do. You may need to be selective. Don't disturb anyone running around or that is with a patient. This definitely won't work in and around A&E!!!

You may have to hang around for a while. Again, it's advised you take an adult with you, but don't let them do the talking! You're the one that wants the interview.

When you do stop someone, the conversation might go something like this:

YOU: *"Excuse me, sorry for stopping you, I know you're busy, but I wonder if you can help me. Do you work in INSERT SECTOR / DEPARTMENT?"*

THEM: *"Yes"*

YOU: *"OK, fab. This may seem like a weird question, but I am really interested in working in this area and I know it is difficult to get work experience, so I am trying to find someone from this area that I can...*

Chapter 11 – STANDING OUT FROM THE CROWD

... interview at some point in the future. I don't know if you would be the person to ask or if you know whom I should talk to?"

It's short and sweet. Make it clear you are happy to hang around if they have to go off somewhere at that moment and wait for them. You can pass your letter on to them and politely ask for their name if they are going to pass you on to someone else. There is nothing stronger than asking to meet someone that you have not met before and mentioning the other person that you had originally met. It's kind of like name-dropping and will improve your chances of getting through to them.

So, these are my top tips. It may seem like a lot of work, but no-one else will do these things. It's doing the hard work up front, to make getting onto your course or getting that job, much easier.

You're running your life the way others won't, so you can do things tomorrow that others can't.

What I mean by this is, that you're living your life with a purpose for a defined goal that drives all your actions – such as the one's outlined in this chapter. None of these are guaranteed to work, but they will improve your chances and doing something with some direction is better than doing nothing other than wishing and hoping.

Chapter 12

Perseverance & Mindset

No matter what you choose to do in life, be that becoming a doctor, vet, banker, teacher, to be a success you will have to overcome some obstacles and challenges that at the time are so tough, horrible and hard that you may consider giving up. However, once you reach your goal and you take a look back, those challenges made you develop into who you are. Those challenges made you stronger as a person and without them your success would not be as awe-inspiring as it is.

You need to have perseverance to succeed and to keep going when you are knocked back again and again and again. As Rocky Balboa says… 'It's not about how hard you can hit, it's about how hard you can get hit and keep moving forward'.

These 'hits' might be biggies such as a duff grade on an assignment or an exam, or could be something small like a bad night's sleep or getting stuck in traffic.

Your determination, drive and attitude to succeed start with your mind-set. You have two choices, you can be a:

- 'why me' / 'the world hates me' type of person

or a

- 'no worries' / 'let's just get on with it' type of person

Chapter 12 – PERSEVERANCE & MINDSET

I am sure you know 'why me' people. In fact, you might have been one, but that's ok because so have I and so has every single other person on the planet. We've all had those moments where you hear that little voice in your head saying - why me? It's just not fair, this always happens to me, my life is ruined! I can't do this, I can't be bothered today, I'm so tired, I'm an idiot and can't do anything right.... and so on and so on.

The thing is, your brain believes what you tell it and having the right mindset towards yourself, your abilities and your ambitions is very, very important.

We are scripted from an early age to have a negative attitude and have these words engrained into our minds. Right from when we are toddlers, we scream IT'S NOT FAIR!! Then we are told life's not fair by parents and peers. It keeps going and going until we actually believe it's true, that life IS unfair and that we are hard done by. It's probably a social norm in western society and is born out of frustration where people desire goods but don't have the dedication or the work ethic (and sometimes are just too damn lazy) to do anything about it.

We've all said these things to ourselves but I find it so strange that we put ourselves down or put our mind in a place where we are not motivated. As weird as it sounds, we usually do it to sound 'attractive' to our friends.

Just listen to your friends, family or other people's conversations over the next few days and see how many times they say something about themselves that is de-motivating or they put themselves down.

It isn't anyone's fault, just that many of us don't stop and think about what we have actually said. Take the saying 'life's not fair'. That it is a pretty big statement to make. Chances are you are healthy, without illness. You are at a school where your teachers want you to succeed. You have parents that love you, a house that is warm, safe and has food on the table. You have friends you enjoy being with and you have all this technology around you that either makes your life easier or can give you information at the click of a button.

Your life is pretty awesome if you ask me.

Before you start yelling at me, or sending hate mail, I KNOW there will be some of you that will read this book and your parents have split up, you don't get on with some of your teachers. Or you may be being bullied or your home struggles financially.

Giving advice in this area can be very difficult as every circumstance is different but what I will say is, don't let circumstances or other people's agendas affect who you are or what you want to achieve. It may be tough to get through, but keep fighting and striving for what you want in life.

What makes the difference between the 'why me's' and the 'no worries' is the conscious decision to not let circumstances dictate how their life should be. They make a conscious choice to react in a way that is positive and moves them forward, that there has to be a solution to the problem... they react in a way that is in line with how they want their life to pan out.

Here is THE BIGGEST shift you can make with your attitude to life and your mindset.

Do you know what the chances are of you being you, here on earth at this very moment in time?

It is about 1 trillion to 1.

A trillion to 1 and you're walking around saying things like I can't be bothered today, I hate this or I hate that.

YOU ARE A 1 TRILLION TO 1 SHOT THAT MADE IT.

Chapter 12 – PERSEVERANCE & MINDSET

The number of things that had to have happened for you to be you as you are today is truly staggering. Think about it (warning … this next bit might make you throw up a little in your mouth)

Your Mom and Dad had to meet randomly at some point.

They fell in love and you know…. **did it**….

They did it at a specific time so your Dad's sperm could fertilise your Mom's egg

The egg was released from one of millions in her ovaries

This egg survived 'dying' off in your mom's pre-puberty years as females are born with about 2 million eggs, but about 11,000 die off each month in the run up to puberty.

The sperm was one of about 20 million that your Dad released.

All of these factors made you.

I'll say it again (not the bit about your Mom and Dad getting jiggy)…

YOU ARE A 1 TRILLION TO 1 SHOT.

How amazing is that?

Just sit and think about this for a moment. How does it make you feel? Does putting yourself down feel a little bit stupid now? It should, but not for too long though. We have all made this mistake.

So, next time you feel like you're demotivated or the world is against you, remember you are a 1 trillion to 1 shot.

You made it. That specific sperm, that specific egg at that specific time resulted in you being here.

And then on top of that, you're only here once! As my father-in-law puts it quite bluntly: "You're born, you live, you die".

Chapter 12 – PERSEVERANCE & MINDSET

So simple, but you get no 2nd chances at this. This is it. Some of you might have other beliefs about afterlives and other jiggery-pokery but you are here now.

This is it and I use it to help me make decisions about what I want to do. Let me give you an example.

In any situation where I am struggling to find motivation to do something, I think when I am on my death bed in (hopefully!) many years' time will I regret not doing the thing I am struggling with?

You cannot have any regrets in life, so put yourself in that position. Imagine you are 90+ years old on your deathbed with your family around you and you are talking about your life.

Are you talking about regretting that you didn't achieve that dream job, ask that girl out, talk to that boy in the other class, buy that dream house, drive that amazing car, live the life that you want.

Or, are your talking about all the amazing things you did in your life, all the people you helped in your job, all the amazing experiences you had.

All because you were motivated and COULD BE BOTHERED.

Think of life like this and yours will never be the same again.

Chapter 13

It's All Part of The Masterplan

As Noel Gallagher says in what I reckon is his best song *"It's all part of the Masterplan"* (seriously, if you've not heard Oasis's song Masterplan, check it out now on YouTube!)

You need a Masterplan. Just follow the steps in Chapter 9 to put yours together. By having a plan and goal set out you can react to any situation by considering how it is going to help you get to your goal. Do you sit in the corner, sucking your thumb, rocking back and forth, or do you grab the situation by the throat, deal with it and move on. The choice is yours.

NB: You have to have a clear mind (remember, silence is golden?!) to do this.

Try this: when you are faced with a situation that frustrates you, or is one of those 'why me' moments, take a couple of seconds to hold your thoughts. Just stop. Don't say anything, try and remove the 'why me' from your mind. Think: is that the right attitude and decision to make? Your reaction is going to shape your mind, your attitude and your future.

I know that it can be tricky to do, and it will take some time to get into the habit of pausing for a moment every time a tough situation appears. I still struggle with it, every now and then for a fleeting moment the 'why me' pops up in my head and I have to banish it back to where it came from.

Believe me, this WILL make a difference to your life and outlook on things. You will find yourself being more positive, calmer and more relaxed. It's almost as if your brain stops fighting everything and just lets you get on with life, and allows you to deal with whatever comes your way.

You may want to reflect on this as well. You may totally and utterly forget to do this in some situations, or you can think back to a time when you have reacted in a negative way. You can reflect afterwards and think - how could I have reacted differently? Why did I react like that? Did it help me? If I acted more positively, would my situation now be any different?

You will start to notice when other people react with a 'why me' attitude to their situation as well. I know I do. When this does happen, I have two thoughts. First, I want to shake them and say **DON'T BE SO STUPID!!** (I don't obviously). And secondly, I have a little smile to myself and think - I'm soooo glad I don't act like that. Their life must feel awful if they think that what has just happened has ruined their life in an overly dramatic way.

So, who are you?

Are you a whiney, why me, I hate everyone, blah, blah, blah type of person?

Or are you a positive, I can deal with anything life throws at me, let's do it, grab the bull by the horns, deal with it, close the deal, study hard, play hard, my life is awesome, I know what I want – type of person?

The choice is yours, and that is the biggest factor here.

YOU ARE 100% RESPONSIBLE FOR WHAT HAPPENS TO YOU IN YOUR LIFE.

It is yours to treasure and do with what you wish, you only have one shot!

Now, take a moment to read those lines again and just sit and think about it.

It's a big and uncomfortable statement to make, because deep down we all know it's true. Obviously, as discussed, there are some things we cannot control in life. Things like family illnesses, accidents & other people's decisions.

But you can control YOUR choices. What you want to do for a career, where you want to study, how hard you study, how late you stay out, what you eat and drink, how much exercise your do, how many (and what sort of) books you read, how long you spend on the internet, how many phone calls you make, how many letters you write asking for work experience or interviews…The list goes on and on.

Just keep that one statement in your mind.

You are 100% responsible for what happens to you in your life.

Go out and…

#BeMoreMaverick

Chapter 14

Pass Your Exams in 90 minutes

I am serious! You can pass all your exams by studying for 90 minutes!

OK, OK… I'm not talking about one single round revision for 90 minutes, but what about 226 sets of 90 minutes spread over a year.

Why 226?…Let us do some maths…

- There are 365 days in the year.
- Let's ditch the weekends and lose 104 days. That leaves 261 days.
- Next, lets ditch 6 weeks for the summer holidays, as well as 5 days for Christmas and New Year. That is a total of 35 days.
- 35 from 261 leaves us with 226.
- That's 226 days, studying for 90 minutes each day.

Could you master or at least get a far better understanding of your subjects if you did 226 sessions studying them.

I bet you could.

It is such a simple concept. But it requires some discipline. 90 minutes every day for at least 5 days a week, including all the school holidays (except the 6 weeks and 5 days over Christmas and New Year of course.).

What's that I hear you say…. You don't have time? I'm going to be blunt here…. But I smell BS!

Any one that says they don't have time is a total liar, liar pants on fire! Just think about your day at the moment. Where could you fit 90 minutes in?

Let's say you get home at 4:30pm and go to bed around 10pm, you've got 5 ½ hours to kill! Doing 90 minutes of work still leaves you 4 hours to do what you want. Go to your sports club, play computer games, go on social media, Netflix and chill….

I also heard you say "Tom, you forgot about taking off the other school holidays!"

Errrrrr, no I didn't

Listen, if you want to be successful and get the results you need to get your dream job there are some sacrifices you have to make.

And to be honest it is not a big sacrifice.

Let's do the maths…. again….

We ditched the summer hols and 5 days at Christmas so that leaves:

- October half term - 5 days
- Christmas – 5 days
- Feb half term – 5 days
- Easter – 10 days
- May half term – 5 days

- So, that is 30 days in total.
- Let's say you were awake for 16 hours of each day (getting your 8 hours sleep!)
- 16 hours x 30 days = 480 hours
- 480 hours x 60minutes = 28,800 minutes that you're awake.
- If we look at our 90 minutes as a percentage of this....
- 90 minutes x 30 days = 2,700 minutes
- 2,700 / 28,800 = 0.093
- 0.093 x 100 = 9.3%

9.3% of your holidays on studying.

9.3% of your time awake in the holidays taking small but significant steps towards your dream job.

It's not much to ask, is it?

Now, would you like an extra 15 days in the year?

I'm not talking 15 normal days. I'm talking about 15 solid days of extra work & revision, 24/7, no breaks.

You can do it! Honestly you can.

Do ya wanna know how?

Get up one hour early every day for 365 days of the year. This totals 365 hours or 15 days (365 / 24 if you want to do the maths) of extra time to do what you want.

Revise, do your 90 minutes, play sport, play video games... whatever it is... it is making room in your day to do your 90 minutes either straight away or in the evening.

Admittedly, this is a bit hard-core, so let's say you did this for half of the year. That's 182.5 days, which is just shy of a school year... funny that, eh?

You could look at this the other way around and get up 1 hour early in the… dare I say it…. School holidays!!!!

Imagine that… getting up at 6am every day of the school holidays, doing your 90 minutes of school work done and dusted by 8am each day.

Trust me… you will feel so satisfied (and a little bit smug!).

Plus, you've got the rest of the day to do what you want! Go back to bed, hang out, Netflix and chill.

Plus, by doing it first thing you have a better chance of not being distracted by friends on social media or family barging in. It is surprisingly quiet at 6 in the morning. Plus, your brain is in the most optimal state for learning first thing in the morning.

I know what you're also thinking… Why 90 minutes, Tom?

Good question. It is the perfect amount of time where your brain can cope with prolonged concentration before it starts to drift and nothing else goes in.

You need it to be undisturbed time too.

Did you know that when you're deep in concentration on a piece of work and you're disturbed, it takes a full 15 minutes for you to get back to the same state of mind as you were in before.

Not good.

So, here are my Golden Rules for your 90 minutes.

1. Tell your family what you're doing.
2. Plan it out.
3. Get into a routine.
4. No phones.
5. No Music or TV.

Here are some finer details.

1. **Tell your family what you are doing.** Tell them that when you are working you're not to be disturbed in ANY circumstances!

No, "do you want a drink"

No, "I've bought you a snack"

No, "how are you getting on"

No, "Can you take the rubbish out"

NO NOTHING!!!!

The only time you should be disturbed is if it is a life or death situation.

Make a sign for your door…. Or even download our one from www.medicalmavericks.co.uk/book

2. **Plan out when you're doing your 90 minutes and what you're going to do.**

It could just be as simple as looking at a different subject each day. Mondays is Chemistry, Tuesdays – Biology etc. etc.

Or be more specific on a particular area you're struggling with. The important thing is plan what you're doing and when you're doing it. Do this last thing on Friday, Saturday morning or Sunday night. It doesn't matter when, just as long as it is before the start of the next week.

You can download our weekly planning template here: www.medicalmavericks.co.uk/book

3. **Get into a routine.** Try to stick to the same time each day, that way everyone knows what you're doing.

4. **Your mobile phone.** Yes, I am going there…

I know you'll probably get this all the time but I am deadly serious about this one.

TURN IT OFF.

One of the biggest things about your 90 minutes is that it is concentrated time and effort on your work. Surely you can survive without messaging someone, sending a snapchat, posting a selfie or just checking out the Internet in whatever way you do.

I know it is a habit. We all have this amazing device that can tell us anything we want and is such a powerful tool, but we spend our time looking at cat videos or sending silly pictures to each other.

I'm not perfect. I do it, put my hand in my pocket and just start tapping away.

Have you ever just thought, "WTF was I doing there? How has seeing what Jane in class 10C is moaning about or what Dan is 11D got up to on his hols, or seeing that kid get smacked in the head by a flying football (even though it was funny as hell!) helped me anyway?"

I have to tell myself to stop. You have to tell yourself to stop.

Turn it off. Not mute, not silence.

TURN

IT

OFF !!!

5. Silence is golden.

No music, no study groups with friends, no background distractions. You'll only spend the first 10 minutes picking your tunes or start chatting about random shizzle.

Again, I can hear you saying.... "But Tom I need music to concentrate" or "I like studying with my friends!"

Sniff Sniff, what's that smell?.... I smell BS again....

I am going to be **extremely** blunt here.

You don't like studying with your friends... you like being with your friends because it creates some kind of distraction from this 'evil' studying task in front of you!

On the music side of things many people have been brainwashed into thinking they need some kind of background music to concentrate.

It is utter rubbish.

In your exams, are you going to be listening to some bangin' tune whilst describing the functions of the heart?

How can you learn those chemistry formulas, or what E=MC2 is all about or how the liver works when you're singing the lyrics to Justin Bieber or Little Mix?

When you qualify as a doctor, nurse, paramedic or healthcare scientist and you're treating a patient, you're not going to stop what you're doing and shout across the ward **"This is a TUUUUUNNE!! Turn it up!"** and then start throwing some shapes around.

Your brain just can't cope with distractions when it needs to concentrate!!!!

It can only concentrate on a small number of things at a time, so don't add to what it has to do in your 90 minutes!!

In my opinion, this has all come from the society 'needing' to be constantly entertained or stimulated. How often in your day are you in a place of silence? I would bet my house on it that it is never.

Walking to school – got your headphones on.

In school – always with your friends

Get home – TV is on, family are talking to you.

Everyone, including me, gets very little time when they are truly in silence.

And this is a big problem.

To be truly successful you need to be comfortable with your own thoughts and be happy in silence without distraction.

Don't worry I am not going all Buddhist Monk on you, but their principles are bang on.

You need to get used to being on your own, in silence, for 90 minutes where there is just you, your desk, your books, paper and pens. Nothing else.

After about a week of doing this I can guarantee you'll be a different person and you'll crave those short periods of time.

You can thank me when you pass your exams.

Even though doing your 90-minute study sessions is a small ask each day, you probably will need a bit of motivation and reward.

So, each week pick something as a reward… it might be a film on Netflix (I like Netflix, can you tell?), that chocolate bar in the cupboard that has been calling to you, spending a tenner on yourself at Pri-marni….

It doesn't have to be big. But when you do 5 out of 5 sessions give yourself a reward.

Anything less…. No reward. Nothing… Nada…. Zilch.

Obviously, there are the little rewards you can give yourself in your head for each 90 minute session.

I can guarantee you will feel a little smug each time you complete a session, as you know some, if not all of your friends won't have done it.

((That is unless you pass on this book or tell your friends to get one and tell them to read this chapter, then you'll all be doing it!... Thanks in advance!))

And when times get tough and you really don't want to do it just remember you are taking tiny steps towards your dream job.

Small concentrated periods of effort each day will result in massive progress.

Try it… I dare you!

- **Plan it out on a Sunday.**
- **Get into a routine.**
- **Get up early.**
- **Get it done.**
- **Reward yourself.**
- **Pass your exams.**
- **Get a great job!**

Chapter 15

What to Do If You Have Pushy Parents

Before we get started on this chapter, let's make one thing clear. Your parents love you and only want what they see is best for you.

And this is the problem. It is what THEY see is best and not **WHAT IS BEST** for you.

I see this time and time again in my visits to careers fairs, talks and visits across the UK. We'll have a stand which is promoting careers in the NHS and a parent will come to the stand with their child and proudly say, "My son/daughter here wants to be a doctor."

And usually that is it.

All they have told me is that their child wants to be a doctor with a big beaming proud smile on their face (the parent's face that is!).

The reaction in my head is "yeah… and…."

It is as if they want us to do a dance around and shout from the roof tops: "we've got another one… this kid wants to be a doctor!!"

And this is the 1st problem.

It is more than likely a status thing for the parent. Yes, being a doctor is an amazing achievement in society and for some cultures especially. Saying your child is a doctor is a very proud moment. The parent feels elevated, almost.

But this is wrong IF the child hasn't really had their say.

You may have experienced this conversation with your parents whilst talking about your future career. It might go something like this...

Parent: Have you thought about what you want to do for a job?

You: Not really, I quite like trying out my lessons for a bit.

Parent: Really? No idea at all?

You (in your head): I'm 15 FFS... I can't decide which socks to wear in the morning sometimes and you want me to make a decision now on what to do with the next 30-40 years of my life.

You (out loud): Hmmm, I do quite like music, art, drama & English.

Parent: I think you'd make a good doctor. Why don't you become a doctor? A doctor would be good!

You (in your head): WTAF... there is no way I want to be a doctor. I like science, but not that much.

You (Out loud): Really? I'm not sure about that. You need top top grades. Literally A*s / level 9's across all subjects.

Parent: I'm sure you can do it if you knuckle down a bit more.

You: Maybe...

Parent: OK, then... we'll get you sorted as a doctor. Wait till the ladies / lads down the pub / club / church / synagogue / mosque / office hear that my little *insert your name here* is going to be a doctor.

Chapter 15 – What To Do If You Have Pushy Parents

And that's it…. Your future decided.

You can't blame your parents. They probably know very little about the careers in the NHS. Do a little test on them. Ask them to write down all the careers they know about in the NHS… and I mean exact job titles. I bet they can't get more than 10.

Then get them to read this book… especially chapters 2 to 7.

Once they've done this you've got some ammunition to go back to them with and say:

"Being a doctor is right for me, I like these careers in here (use the book) and this one and this one".

Or, you can say:

"I've had a look through this book as well as the NHS careers website and I really don't fancy any of the medical careers. Being a doctor is not for me, neither are any of the careers in here. I want to explore my options some more."

It is OK to disagree with your parents and it is OK to not want to be a doctor. Just go to them with some evidence that you've done your research.

I know it could be difficult to disagree with what your parents say. It takes a lot of courage to 'stand up' to them and speak your own mind. You may be frightened to do so because it turns into an argument or you don't want to disappoint them, or even worse they use emotional blackmail by telling you you've brought shame on the family and they threaten to outcast you.

But in any situation like this I have one thought… and it is a bit grim.

One day your folks won't be here and you'll be on your own (metaphorically… you'll probably have a partner and kids of your own by now, but you get my point…)

Yep – they'll be gone and they won't be able to judge your decisions, they won't be able to judge you.

Let's say you do become a doctor (or any other careers your parents chose for you… a lawyer, engineer, architect…) and you are 37 years old. Both your parents pass away. You now have half your working life and over half of your actual life ahead of you.

Another 30-50 years of time to do stuff. Work, play, rest and enjoy.

And you are going to spend all this time… and it is a loooooooong time, doing something that you didn't want to do in the first place and that you don't want to do now but did it to please someone else that now isn't here and won't care one bit because they are not here.

How messed up is that? Not that we're talking about your parents not being here, but the fact is you will more than likely spend over half your life doing something you don't want to in order to please someone that is now dead.

It is properly messed up and so wrong.

There's none of this, "but they're looking over me…"

What do you think is going to happen? They're going to haunt you and shame you from 'the other side'?

Absolute codswallop.

Chapter 15 – What To Do If You Have Pushy Parents

If that actually happens… how many times has someone experienced this. I'll tell you.

NON… NADA… ZILCH… no one has ever said I was haunted by my folks because I chose a different career.

It is a societal thing for both you and your parents.

Promise me if you are in this situation, you'll sit down quietly and just think about this situation as I have laid it out here. I am sure you'll think differently about this decision.

Back to the careers fairs I was talking about earlier…

If a parent comes up and tells me their child is going to be doctor, I immediately look at the child to see their reaction.

I don't look at the parent… I look straight into the kid's eyes and say:

"Really? Is that right? YOU want to become a doctor?" That isn't a condescending 'you' it is a 'have you made that decision?' you.

I don't look at the parent… I don't have to because I can see in my peripheral vision the glare and stare they are currently doing at the back of the kids head. I am sure they think their stare is controlling the kids mind!!!

The standard answer is a timid "yes".

My next question is "Do you know what you have to do to become a doctor?"

The standard is "No"

I then go into a 5 minute explanation of the whole process and that it is a decision they shouldn't make quickly.

Sometimes, the kids parents bring up to see us are not even in secondary school. They're 10 and 11 years old.

They've not experienced all the fab subjects you study at secondary school that don't even get a look in at primary.

How the F*#$ can a 10 year old decide on what they want to do for the next 60 years of their life.

However, what I always do is finish with these few lines.

"To be a doctor you need top, top grades and many students just like you don't make it. I didn't make it. Now you shouldn't give up on working in healthcare if that is what YOU want to do. There are over 300 jobs in the NHS, many are very well paid and there is lots of progression up the seniority scale. So take a look at this list or this website to find out more".

I then finish by saying:

"It is OK to change your mind about what you want to do at any point in your life. Whether it be a doctor or an artist, a designer, musician, actor, lawyer or whatever. The important thing is that YOU make the decision as it is your life and you need to have the courage to follow what you want to do".

Chapter 16

For Parents:
You Want Your Child to Be a Doctor

I've written this chapter for any parent that wants their child to be a doctor or have effectively made the decision for their child on what they want to be when they are older without any input from their child.

You might not know you've done it. But if you stop for a moment and honestly ask yourself is this what my child REALLY wants to do… or is it what I want them to do, I hope you discover the right answer.

I do want to set out at the start that I know you only want the best for your child and would do anything for them. You want them to be safe, secure and happy. It is what I want for my kids. At the time of writing I have a 7 year old girl and one on the way so I know the feelings us parents have when we look at our kids and think what they might do with their lives, both when we are old and wrinkly and when we are gone.

But, if you are a parent that has pretty much made up your child's mind for them… I'm here to burst your bubble…. You might not like it, but it is the truth.

Firstly…. chances are, you probably know very little about the jobs that are out in the world and I am pretty certain you have no idea what kind of careers are coming down the tracks in the next 10, 20, 30 years' time.

Don't believe me? Let's stick with the NHS for now. Name 10 job titles in the NHS … and I mean proper job titles. Not Doctor, not nurse … I mean actual proper job titles like Histocompatability and Immunogeneticist or what about Cytopathologist…

Both of these are awesome careers by the way. The first one matches organ donor transplants in a lab by using cells from both the donor and recipient. Imagine how proud you would be saying your child helps save people's lives by making sure organs don't get rejected in transplants!

The 2nd one looks for cancerous cells. Imaging how proud you would be, knowing your child is helping fight cancer and saving lives!

If you don't know what is out there, how does your child know… how do your child's teachers know!! That is one reason for writing this book. I want to show you how many amazing careers there are in the NHS. It's not your fault you don't know what else is out there, but because you don't, that doesn't mean you have to revert to the standard stock answer – become a doctor.

As a society, we are almost programmed to see doctors as this all knowing super person, almost a demi-god in some people's eyes. Don't get me wrong, doctors have worked oh so hard to get where they are and have the skills to save people's lives, perform unbelievable surgery and cure disease. They really are very special people.

When we talk to friends, family and colleagues about our kids I am sure there is a moment of pride that swells up inside as we say our kid wants to be a doctor and the reactions of those being told this have an equal kind of reaction of 'WOW'.

But this is all **BONKERS!!**

I am sure many parents that experience this, have not let their kid decide the career they want to go down and have told them they should become a doctor because of the crazy self-centred notion of what it does to their status in society and how other people see them and your family.

It is so selfish to expect your child to follow a career path, however rewarding it is financially & socially, because of how it makes you feel, or how other people see you and your family when deep down it was not what your child wanted to do with their life.

And here's another truth bomb… it is THEIR life!

I know in some cultures the mother and father figure are very dominant and make many decisions for their child throughout their early years and teen years. It is very tough for the child to express their feelings and desires. It is stifling for them, causes frustration and in the end, they settle for their lot in life and don't follow or satisfy their desires.

But all of this is to the detriment of the child.

Making decisions about anything in life can be quite tricky. We need practice at it as we grow to build confidence, to help us assess risk and to be able to judge what to do.

Now imagine this.

When you're gone, because one day that will happen, we will be leaving our sons & daughters to fend for themselves. Yes, they might have their own families, but essentially, the people that they have relied upon to make decisions, guide them in life and support them (that's you and me by the way!) will no longer be there.

Surely as parents, our role is to make sure our kids are able to make decisions for themselves, follow their instincts and ultimately be happy in their life!

How can someone be happy doing something that deep down they don't want to do or didn't want to do. Our kids want to make us happy. From an early age we are always telling our children how proud we are of them when they complete some work at school, we always tell them how clever they are and how brilliant their work is.

This makes the kids feel special and want to please us more and more because, let's face it, it feels nice to be told these things. It builds their confidence and we should tell our kids these things.

But the problem is, both us as parents and our kids, let this spill into other areas of our lives. Our kids look to us to help make decisions about all sorts of things and when we advise or TELL them what to do, they do it to please us.

It is a tricky parenting skill that pretty much all of us suck at! We've trained our kids to almost become 'yes men' that want to please us.

When they don't do what we've advised or TOLD them what to do, we get frustrated because we are so used to having them do as we say.

This is where kids start to rebel, arguments occur and frustrations on both sides come to the boil. They know their own mind and need to be able to express it and explore what they are good at.

It all stems from not knowing what else is out there for our kids to explore and discover.

But that doesn't mean we should push our kids down that route.

One final thing....

As parents we think we know what our children like doing at school and have a pretty good idea of what they are good at. However, if you think about it, this isn't really true.

Our kids spend a good 6-8 hours of each day at school with their teachers and friends. They probably in truth spend only 2-3 hours in our company each day. The only feedback you get from the school is via a report or parents evenings. If you ask your child what they did at school today, it is like asking them to remember what they did at 2.42pm on a Sunday in June 7 years ago!

When you look at it this way, it is very difficult for us as parents to get a gauge on what they really enjoy, what they really want to develop, what they want to get better at and explore more deeply.

They may have hidden talents, that with a bit of nurturing, would allow them to follow an amazing career.

How do you know you haven't got a budding musician, an amazing dancer, a talented artist, actor or play write. Your child could be very creative. I speak to teachers that are so frustrated by parents that don't let their children take artistic subjects when they have a talent for it because guess what… They want them to become doctors.

I cannot imagine suppressing any talents or making any of my kids do what they don't want to do because of some cultural / societal belief that becoming a doctor is the ultimate status symbol.

Take a look through this book, have a chat with your child about what they like to do and re-assure them that you'll support their decisions in any way you can and help them become what they want to be whether it is a doctor or not.

Chapter 17

The 40 Amazing Careers

This is where we get deep down and dirty with all 40 careers. They have been split into their corresponding subsectors and are all colour coded.

Each career covers two pages and includes basic info on what the career entails, typical routes into the career, suggested alternatives as well as some amazing facts and other bonus resources.

We mainly focus on Healthcare Science careers, but there are several pages dedicated to giving an overview of some of the other NHS sectors including Medicine, Ambulance Services, Management careers and many more!

At the very end of the careers in this chapter there are even more resources that you can use to help guide you to an awesome career. These include videos on our website and workshops that can be delivered at your school or college.

So, what are you waiting for? Turn the page to start looking at the 40 awesome NHS careers that you never knew existed.

NB: The pay scales included in these pages may have changed from the time of print and should be used as a guide only. Please do your own research on the websites included at the end of the chapter to see up to date pay scales!!!

Area of HCS: Physiological Science
Pay scale: Bands 5-9 £22k - £100k

AMAZING FACT

Some hearing aids conduct sound through the mastoid bone. This is the bony bit behind your ear and it conducts sound into your inner ear!

Working with children through to the elderly, audiologists identify hearing and balance function and the range of issues that can occur with their patients. They then have to recommend and provide a course of rehabilitation or management.

They work with patients with many different types of hearing disorders, such as tinnitus (ringing ears). They can enable severely audibly impaired people regain a sense of sound by recommending cochlea implants.

Not only do they have to work out the problems patients might have, they may help to develop a new alternative for the problem.

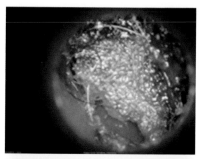

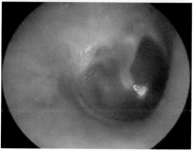

AMAZING FACT 2

Did you know that as you get older you gradually lose the ability to higher frequency sounds. This was physiological phenomenon was used to design 'The Mosquito', an anti-social behaviour deterrent that emitted a certain frequency of sound that only teenagers could hear! The noise was so annoying it stopped groups congregating in areas where is was placed for example shops.

What to do to get into this career...

GCSE

Grades 9-4 / A-C in Maths, English & Science

A – Levels or BTEC Biology, Chemistry recommended

Practitioner Training Programme on a Healthcare Science BSc degree in Life Sciences

A subject related BSc University Degree Qualification First or 2:1

Scientist Training Programme (STP) on a MSc Course at University

Top Tip

Check out the other Physiology careers including cardiology, neurophysiology and respiratory physiology.

VIDEO

To see the difference a hearing aid can make to someone's life, check out the video we found of a 6 month old baby having their hearing aid fitted for the first time. You can see the epic moment they start to hear their Mother's voice for the 1st time! An audiologist would have been involved in making this happen. Check out www.medicalmavericks.co.uk/book

Cardiac Scientist

Area of HCS: Physiological Science
Pay scale: Bands 2-7 £16k - £42k with senior roles up to Band 9 £100k

AMAZING FACT

A 12 lead ECG actually only has 10 cables. The 12 "lead" is due to the 12 different voltage traces you get.

These guys are at the heart of a hospital. They carry out tests daily on patient's that diagnose or monitor patients hearts from babies to the elderly.

Although they work alongside a range of healthcare professionals, they often interact with the patients using a range of different medical test from electrocardiograms (See Right Top) and echocardiograms (See Right Bottom) to pacemaker implantation and exercise stress tests.

As with every area of medicine there is often chance to work within research which enables the patients to receive top quality healthcare.

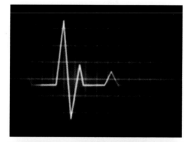

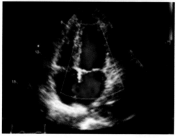

SEARCH

You can find out more about how the heart works and actually see a video of Tom's heart beating on the screen by going to www.medicalmavericks.co.uk/book
There are a couple of video's as well as a PDF download of the cardiac cycle.

What to do to get into this career...

GCSE

Grades 9-4 / A-C in Maths, English & Science

A – Levels or BTEC Biology, Chemistry recommended

Practitioner Training Programme on a Healthcare Science BSc degree in Life Sciences

A subject related BSc University Degree Qualification First or 2:1

Scientist Training Programme (STP) on a MSc Course at University

Top Tip

Check out the other Physiology careers including cardiology, neurophysiology and respiratory physiology.

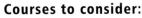

Courses to consider:
Human Physiology
Human Biology
Exercise Physiology
Exercise Science
Sports Science

Clinical Perfusion Scientist

Area of HCS: Physiological Science
Pay scale: Bands 7+ £32k - £70k

AMAZING FACT

On average, the human heart beats 36,792,000 times per year, 100,800 times per day, 4,200 times per hour and 70 times per minute.

In open heart surgery, you will need some help in pumping your blood round your body whilst the heart is being worked on. This is where these guys come in, they look after your circulation whilst the operation is going on.

With the help of a large number of sophisticated machines, (See Right) they take over a patients lung and heart functions. They literally sustain the life of a person whose heart has been stopped. When you hear the words 'going onto bypass' on hospital TV dramas, it is these guys saying that.

They are taking the blood out of the body, oxygenating it in a machine, and then putting it back in whilst the heart or lungs are being operated on! That is some serious responsibility.

You have to be a serious team player in this career working alongside anaesthetists, surgeons and theatre staff to keep the patient alive and safe. Communication and being able to keep calm and give clear instructions is also key.

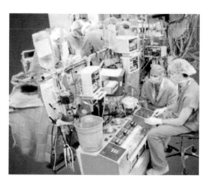

It's not just adults that need heart surgery. New born babies are common patients, having to have defects in their heart repaired fairly soon after birth.

SEARCH

There is a dedicated website for Clinical Perfusion. You can check it out by going to www.scps.org.uk It has more info on what these peeps get up to as well as links to jobs vacancies.

112

What to do to get into this career...

GCSE

Grades 9-4 / A-C in Maths, English & Science

AMAZING FACT 2

Around 33,000 open heart operations are performed each year in the UK and there are around 3,000 clinical perfusionists.

A – Levels or BTEC Biology, Chemistry recommended

A subject related BSc University Degree Qualification First or 2:1

Alternative courses to Consider at University:
Human Biology
Human Physiology
Biomedical Science
Clinical Science

Apply for a Trainee programme with an NHS Trust.

Study based training that leads to a post-graduate qualification. You are paid whilst you train.

Critical Care Scientist

Area of HCS: Physiological Science
Pay scale: Bands 2-7 £16k - £42k with senior roles up to Band 9 £100k

AMAZING FACT | A Spanish cyclist, Miguel Indurain was recorded as having a resting heart rate of 29 BPM!!

A critical care scientist has a massively varied role within a critical care setting. They work directly with patients whilst also having a part to play with the running of technology in the department and providing advice to other members of the team.

Critical care is also known at intensive care or ITU (the U stands for unit), so the patients here are very, very poorly. Therefore a critical care scientist needs to have a great understanding of human physiology and how drugs affect the body.

On the other hand, they also need good knowledge of the technology and equipment being used, as they are one of the first ports of call for maintenance and advice. This is a key role, as some of the equipment would include ventilators that are keeping patients alive!

There's just so much these peeps do, we can't fit it all in here!!

Examples of Equipment used in ITU:

Ventilator - artificially breathes for the patient when unconscious

Drug Driver Syringe - delivers drugs to patient when a button is pressed

ECG Monitor - records the electrical signals from a patients heart

Feeding Tubes & Suction Pumps

What to do to get into this career...

GCSE

Grades 9-4 / A-C in
Maths, English
& Science

**A – Levels or
BTEC Biology,
Chemistry
recommended**

**Practitioner
Training
Programme on a
Healthcare Science
BSc degree in Life
Sciences**

**A subject
related BSc
University
Degree
Qualification
First or 2:1**

**Scientist
Training
Programme
(STP) on a MSc
Course at
University**

Top Tip

Check out the other Physiology
careers including cardiology,
neurophysiology and
respiratory physiology.

SEARCH

You can find out even more
about this career by going
to the Society of Critical Care
Technologists. Their website is
www.criticalcaretech.org.uk It
has the latest news, info on the
career itself as well as further
links to other useful sites.

Gastrointestinal Physiologist

Area of HCS: Physiological Science
Pay scale: Bands 2-7 £16k - £42k with senior roles up to Band 9 £100k

AMAZING FACT

An adult intestine measure the length of about 7.5m (25ft), of which the small intestine measures 6m (20ft).

These guys go from top to bottom, following the entry of food at the mouth and the exit at the anus and all that falls in between. They study the gastrointestinal function and any diseases that are linked to it.

With the use of various tests and specialized equipment, procedures are carried out from: pH tests on stomach fluids to ultrasounds on the intestines. They work as part of a team that would include dieticians, colorectal surgeons and gastroenterologists (these are doctors that specialise in the GI tract).

As this career is looking at the digestive system, you are more than likely to work with patients that are embarrassed & concerned about their condition. With examinations of the anal canal and rectum being part of the job, you would have to be mature and respectful whilst working with the patient.

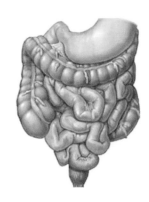

AMAZING FACT 2

The entire surface area of your gastrointestinal tract from your mouth to your anus is approximately 30-40 square meters, which is roughly the size of half the size of a badminton court!

What to do to get into this career...

GCSE

Grades 9-4 / A-C in Maths, English & Science

A – Levels or BTEC Biology, Chemistry recommended

Practitioner Training Programme on a Healthcare Science BSc degree in Life Sciences

A subject related BSc University Degree Qualification First or 2:1

Scientist Training Programme (STP) on a MSc Course at University

Top Tip

Check out the range of courses at University that would be relevant for this career and then check what the entry requirements are for each of them for a more accurate picture.

Alternative courses to Consider at University:
Genetics
Biomedical Science
Immunology
Molecular Biology
Cell Biology
Physiology
Biological Science

Similar careers to look for in Life Sciences:
Biochemistry
Pathology
Haematology
Clinical Immunology
Toxicology
Virology

117

Area of HCS: Physiological Science
Pay scale: Bands 2-7 £16k - £42k with senior roles up to Band 9 £100k

AMAZING FACT

A Human Brain has 86 Billion neurons, building blocks of the nervous system, our closest rival are Elephants with 23 Billion.

The human brain is more powerful than any computer (at the moment anyway). These guys explore how the brain and nerves work and what happens when things go wrong. The patients they work with could have serious conditions such as dementia, multiple sclerosis and strokes or less serious, but still very painful and disabling nerve entrapments or carpel tunnel syndrome.

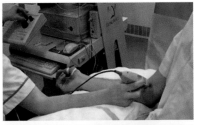

Using sophisticated equipment they carry out test to try and pinpoint the disease. They conduct electromyography (EMG), electroencephalogram (EEG) or evoked potentials - which is where they stimulate a nerve with a tiny electric shock.

VIDEO

We actually met two trainee neurophysiologists from Liverpool and filmed an interview with them along side footage of some of the tests they do. You can see how they can make your hand move with a tiny electric shock to a nerve in your arm and how they read brain wave scans! Check it out by going to www.medicalmavericks.co.uk/book

What to do to get into this career...

GCSE

Grades 9-4 / A-C in Maths, English & Science

Apprentice or Healthcare Science Associate Training

A – Levels or BTEC Biology, Chemistry recommended

Practitioner Training Programme on a Healthcare Science BSc degree in Life Sciences

A subject related BSc University Degree Qualification First or 2:1

Scientist Training Programme (STP) on a MSc Course at University

Alternative courses to Consider at University:
Genetics
Biomedical Science
Immunology
Molecular Biology
Cell Biology
Physiology
Biological Science

Similar careers to look for in Life Sciences:
Biochemistry
Pathology
Haematology
Clinical Immunology
Toxicology
Virology

Ophthalmic and Vision Scientist

Area of HCS: Physiological Science
Pay scale: Bands 2-7 £16k - £42k with senior roles up to Band 9 £100k

AMAZING FACT | An Amazing 70% of the body's receptors are in the eye!!!

A career to keep your eye on, with a diverse range of tests and assessments are used to diagnose and manage conditions such as glaucoma, cataracts and damage to the back of the eye, the retina.

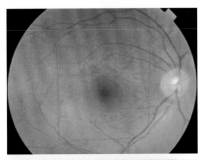

There are some really cool pieces of equipment that can create images of your eye. These include creating a 4-D image of the optic nerve leaving your eye inside your skull, as well as imaging the individual cells that make up your cornea at the front of your eye!

Your cornea is so precious that you only have one set of cells in your cornea for your entire life! They don't renew or regenerate, so look after your corneas!

VIDEO

We met an awesome ophthalmic scientist in Bristol who did all sorts of scans to Tom's eyes as well as answer questions on her job. You can see how the pictures above were taken and what she had to say by visiting www.medicalmavericks.co.uk/book

What to do to get into this career...

GCSE

Grades 9-4 / A-C in
Maths, English
& Science

**A – Levels or
BTEC Biology,
Chemistry
recommended**

**Practitioner
Training
Programme on a
Healthcare Science
BSc degree in Life
Sciences**

**A subject
related BSc
University
Degree
Qualification
First or 2:1**

**Scientist
Training
Programme
(STP) on a MSc
Course at
University**

Top Tip

Check out the other Physiology
careers including cardiology,
neurophysiology and
respiratory physiology.

**Alternative courses to
Consider at University:**
Genetics
Biomedical Science
Immunology
Molecular Biology
Cell Biology
Physiology
Biological Science

**Similar careers to look
for in Life Sciences:**
Biochemistry
Pathology
Haematology
Clinical Immunology
Toxicology
Virology

121

Respiratory Physiologist

Area of HCS: Physiological Science
Pay scale: Bands 2-7 £16k - £42k with senior roles up to Band 9 £100k

AMAZING FACT

People who travel to altitude can stop breathing for up to 30 seconds while sleeping; a phenomenon called periodic breathing.

Working one on one with patients they use a range of tests during rest, exercise and even while patients sleep, to identify lung function problems.

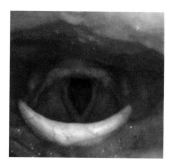

Not only do they help find the main issues with the patients lungs, e.g. asthma or emphysema they also monitor patients to make sure treatment is working and, if it's not, decide what to do.

Some patients struggle with breathing at night and their airway can actually collapse while they sleep. So these scientists set up certain experiments to detect the problem and decide how to manage it, normally with long-term treatments.

VIDEO

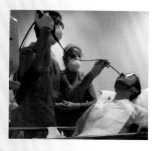

Tom had a series of respiratory tests over 4 weeks at Southampton General Hospital as part of a study in asthma. You can them all including a video of a bronchoscopy, where you get to see inside his lungs! Check out www.medicalmavericks.co.uk/book to see them all!

What to do to get into this career...

GCSE

Grades 9-4 / A-C in
Maths, English
& Science

A – Levels or
BTEC Biology,
Chemistry
recommended

Practitioner
Training
Programme on a
Healthcare Science
BSc degree in Life
Sciences

A subject
related BSc
University
Degree
Qualification
First or 2:1

Scientist
Training
Programme
(STP) on a MSc
Course at
University

Top Tip

Check out the other Physiology
careers including cardiology,
neurophysiology and
respiratory physiology.

**Alternative courses to
Consider at University:**
Genetics
Biomedical Science
Immunology
Molecular Biology
Cell Biology
Physiology
Biological Science

**Similar careers to look
for in Life Sciences:**
Biochemistry
Pathology
Haematology
Clinical Immunology
Toxicology
Virology

Urodynamic Scientist

Area of HCS: Physiological Science
Pay scale: Bands 2-7 £16k - £42k with senior roles
up to Band 9 £100k

AMAZING FACT

Your bladder can hold just
over 1 pint of fluid!

These guys work alongside urologists in diagnosing and treating patients who suffer or have problems with their urinary tract. This normally involves using specialised equipment that can measure the speed at which fluid travels along the urethra and then interpreting the data from these tests to design a treatment plan for patients.

There are other tests that look at pressures within the bladder, even checking whether muscles that control urine output are working properly or not. This can be invasive or non-invasive. The muscles that control if you want to let your urine out or not are called Sphincters.

The patients you work with may be embarrassed about their condition as it could lead to them wetting themselves and having poor bladder control. Therefore you need to be mature, understanding and sympathetic to their condition, treating them with respect and care.

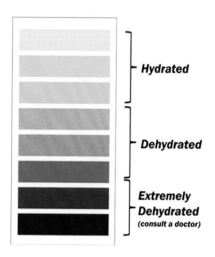

**Scale of hydration from the
colour of your urine**

AMAZING FACT 2

20% of men don't wash their hands after going to the toilet, compared to 10% of women!

124

What to do to get into this career...

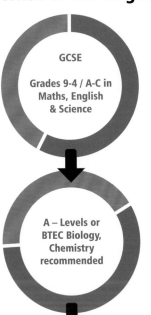

GCSE

Grades 9-4 / A-C in
Maths, English
& Science

**A – Levels or
BTEC Biology,
Chemistry
recommended**

**A subject
related BSc
University
Degree
Qualification
First or 2:1**

**Scientist
Training
Programme
(STP) on a MSc
Course at
University**

Top Tip

Try and get some sort of work
experience or placement within a
medical or hospital setting. This
would be beneficial when applying
for the post graduate course.

AMAZING FACT 3

When you wee, your average flow
rate is around 10-12mL / second....
That's just over half a litre per minute!

Courses to Consider at University:
**Human Biology
Physiology
Biomedical Science**

125

Vascular Scientist

Area of HCS: Physiological Science
Pay scale: Bands 2-7 £16k - £42k with senior roles up to Band 9 £100k

AMAZING FACT | The heart pumps on average 7200 litres of blood per day.

There are 60,000 miles of blood vessels in the human body and these guys explore the lot. They use non-invasive techniques like ultra-sound to examine the blood vessels and blood flow speed.

They are trained to depict and investigate the images that the sound waves bounce back to the computer. The images can be used to diagnose illnesses such as: strokes, aneurysms, and deep thromboses.

Alongside this, they help the future development of non-invasive procedures to assess blood flow and work with surgeons, nurses and other vascular specialists.

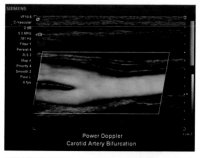

Power Doppler
Carotid Artery Bifurcation

SEARCH

You can find loads of great resources and videos on the heart and blood vessels by visiting www.medicalmavericks.co.uk/book

AMAZING FACT 2

There are approx. 60,000 miles of blood vessels in your body! That is enough to go around the earth two and bit times!

What to do to get into this career...

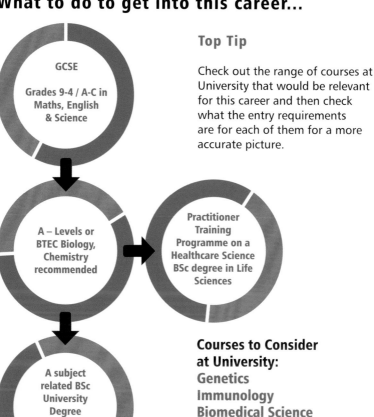

GCSE

Grades 9-4 / A-C in Maths, English & Science

A – Levels or BTEC Biology, Chemistry recommended

Practitioner Training Programme on a Healthcare Science BSc degree in Life Sciences

A subject related BSc University Degree Qualification First or 2:1

Scientist Training Programme (STP) on a MSc Course at University

Top Tip

Check out the range of courses at University that would be relevant for this career and then check what the entry requirements are for each of them for a more accurate picture.

Courses to Consider at University:
Genetics
Immunology
Biomedical Science
Molecular Biology
Cell Biology
Physiology
Biological Science

Similar Careers to look for in Life Sciences:
Biochemistry
Pathology
Haematology
Clinical Immunology
Toxicology
Virology

127

AMAZING FACT

In this career you could be checking for poisons, drug overdoses or even chemical agents that have been used in a terrorist attack!

Ever been bitten by a spider? Well if you have and it was poisonous you'd want to know one of these guys. They design and create wonderful tests to help the Doctors work out which poison the Spider has injected into you.

They also work out tests that can tell what drug overdose a patient has taken. This can be from just looking at the patients pains and groans to tests carried out on expensive specialised equipment.

The majority of their day-to-day work is carried out in a lab, working with a host of varied samples such as: blood, urine, & stomach contents from patients. Occasionally, extracts from the environment are analysed – such as when investigating the source of lead poising of patients near to a suspected contaminated lake or river, for example.

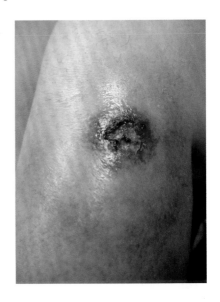

Top Tip

To become an Analytical Toxicologist you usually have to study a science related subject before going onto the Scientific Training Programme (STP). To get onto a STP course you have to apply for a position via the NHS jobs website.

128

What to do to get into this career...

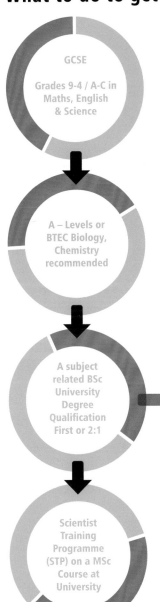

GCSE

Grades 9-4 / A-C in
Maths, English
& Science

A – Levels or
BTEC Biology,
Chemistry
recommended

A subject
related BSc
University
Degree
Qualification
First or 2:1

Scientist
Training
Programme
(STP) on a MSc
Course at
University

Top Tip

Check out the range of courses at
University that would be relevant
for this career and then check
what the entry requirements
are for each of them for a more
accurate picture.

Did you know?

If you study on the Scientific Training
Programme (STP) you actually get
paid to train! How cool is that?

Courses to consider at University:

Biochemistry
Immunology
Forensic Science

Similar careers to look out for in Life Sciences:

Biochemistry
Haematology
Clinical Immunology

AMAZING FACT

All you need to apply for a
trainee post as an APT is GCSEs
in Science, Maths & English

In the words of Bruce Willis "I see dead people," and in this job you really do. APT 's do a range of different jobs in different areas. The top one is helping out to discover how a patient has died, this is done by carrying out a post-mortem.

Do you learn better when doing the job? That's the great thing about APTs, you learn on the job, and as you get more experienced the job changes with you.

As you develop you will work on the day-to-day running of the lab/mortuary (See Right). You work with other healthcare scientists regarding samples and tests, talk with funeral directors as well as the family of the deceased. They will also be responsible for the reconstruction of the deceased, working with legal documents & advising on procedures.

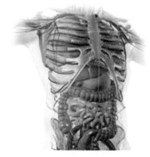

Top Tip

Contact HR departments at hospitals or NHS trusts to search for job opportunities. Check out www.aaptuk.org for more info on becoming an ATP!

What to do to get into this career...

GCSE

Grades 9-4 / A-C in Maths, English & Science (ideally Biology)

Apply for a post as a Trainee APT

At the start of post - observe procedures taking place

Become more involved in procedures under supervision & attend teaching sessions

At the end of your course you will be awarded a qualification in Anatomical Pathology Technology

You will work along side pathologists and your main role will be analysing and examining samples from the deceased to help identify diseases and pathology that could have contributed to their death. You'll use all sorts of equipment including microscopes!

AMAZING FACT

Over half of all deaths attributed to infectious diseases come from tuberculosis, malaria, and AIDS

One of the three Biomedical Scientists: Infection Scientists are one of the unsung heroes of the day-to-day running of a hospital. They are found in the labs hidden away from the public they run test after test to provide rapid diagnosis of an infectious disease so they can find the best treatment for the patient.

Ever had food poisoning? These are the guys who would test stomach samples to find the cause. They also play a key role in running screening for infectious deceases such as HIV & Rubella as well as testing how well treatments battle different infections.

AMAZING FACT 2

There are two specialisms within infection science. The first is medical microbiology, which looks at diseases like meningitis as well as how anti-biotics work. The second is virology, which looks at viral infections including hepatitis and HIV.

AMAZING FACT 3

Did you know that Infection Scientists would be working on outbreaks of diseases like Ebola that occurred in 2014. Ebola is a very deadly viral disease and is extremely infectious. Those infected by the virus end up bleeding internally and externally and usually die because of fluid loss.

What to do to get into this career...

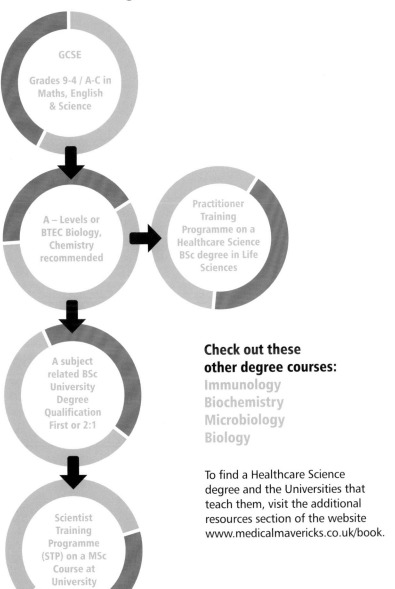

GCSE

Grades 9-4 / A-C in Maths, English & Science

A – Levels or BTEC Biology, Chemistry recommended

Practitioner Training Programme on a Healthcare Science BSc degree in Life Sciences

A subject related BSc University Degree Qualification First or 2:1

Scientist Training Programme (STP) on a MSc Course at University

Check out these other degree courses:

Immunology
Biochemistry
Microbiology
Biology

To find a Healthcare Science degree and the Universities that teach them, visit the additional resources section of the website www.medicalmavericks.co.uk/book.

AMAZING FACT
You can train to be a phlebotomist to take blood at the age of 16!

Blood science is one of the three core biomedical science specialisms and has it's own sub specialisms, which all involve blood. These sub specialisms are Clinical Chemistry, transfusion science, haematology and immunology.

These areas all vary greatly in the conditions they involve but also have lots of cross over. For example, immunology and transfusion science have some cross over when it comes to blood transfusions as the immune system is involved in recognising right or wrong blood types.

Clinical Chemistry is classed under blood sciences as we can test the blood for different chemical markers in different medical tests. These can indicate the health of different organs. A typical example is testing insulin and glucose levels in a diabetic.

AMAZING FACT 2

Red blood cells are awesome. We generate 2.4million of them every second and they live for around 120 days. Then there are the white blood cells. There are around 40 billion of them in our blood. Some of which live for days, others live for up to a year!

VIDEO

Check out what happens to a blood sample in a lab by visiting www.medicalmavericks.co.uk/book You can watch a video and find out about the different tubes that blood is collected in, and how a blood scientist counts how many red blood cells there are in a sample.

What to do to get into this career...

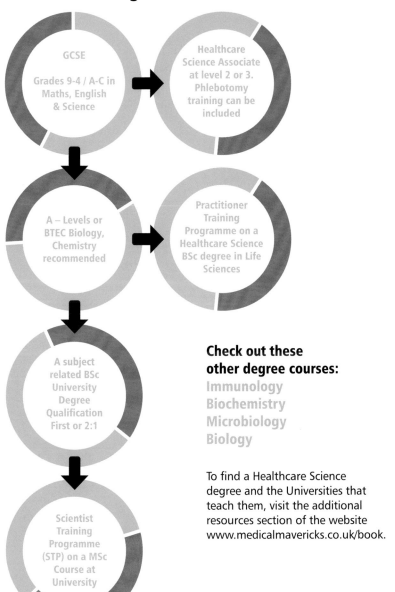

GCSE

Grades 9-4 / A-C in Maths, English & Science

Healthcare Science Associate at level 2 or 3. Phlebotomy training can be included

A – Levels or BTEC Biology, Chemistry recommended

Practitioner Training Programme on a Healthcare Science BSc degree in Life Sciences

A subject related BSc University Degree Qualification First or 2:1

Scientist Training Programme (STP) on a MSc Course at University

Check out these other degree courses:
Immunology
Biochemistry
Microbiology
Biology

To find a Healthcare Science degree and the Universities that teach them, visit the additional resources section of the website www.medicalmavericks.co.uk/book.

AMAZING FACT

These guys & gals use techniques including spectrophotometry, mass spectroscopy, high performance chromatography, electrophoresis & immunoassay.

These guys and girls help diagnose and treat diseases by analysing samples from bodily fluids, blood and urine. The results from these tests would be used by a wide ranging team from pathologists, to surgeons and GPs, who would either diagnose or administer treatments based on the interpretation of the results.

This is a very varied job that encompasses many skills. You will have to be a good communicator with as it the results you produce need to be relayed correctly to other clinicians. You also have some patient contact, which requires empathy and listening skills. You need to be able to write reports as well as be good with numbers.

In addition research can play a massive part of a clinical biochemist work. Without research, we would not have new tests to identify diseases, new or more efficient treatments, making this job vital to patient care.

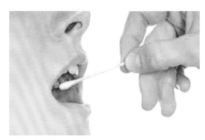

AMAZING FACT 2

There are over 70 different hormones that are produced by the human body. They control everything from when you feel tired, to reproductive cycles, to how leaky your blood vessels are, to how wide your airways are and much more!

136

What to do to get into this career...

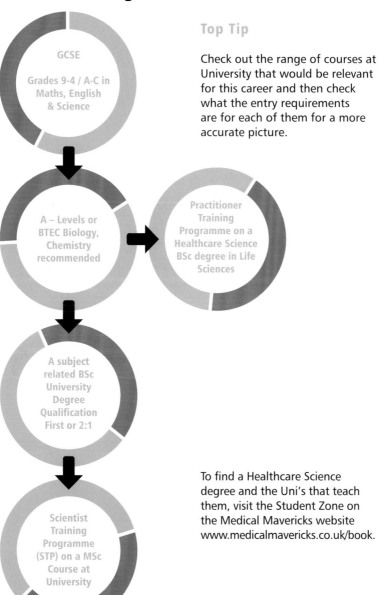

GCSE

Grades 9-4 / A-C in Maths, English & Science

A – Levels or BTEC Biology, Chemistry recommended

Practitioner Training Programme on a Healthcare Science BSc degree in Life Sciences

A subject related BSc University Degree Qualification First or 2:1

Scientist Training Programme (STP) on a MSc Course at University

Top Tip

Check out the range of courses at University that would be relevant for this career and then check what the entry requirements are for each of them for a more accurate picture.

To find a Healthcare Science degree and the Uni's that teach them, visit the Student Zone on the Medical Mavericks website www.medicalmavericks.co.uk/book.

137

AMAZING FACT

The posh name for antibodies is Immunoglobulin or Ig for short. Your body produces five basic types and they are lettered IgA, IgD, IgE, IgG & IgM.

The immune system is the body's main defence against infection. Unfortunately it can get run down and over run. It can even attack your own body and cause all sorts of diseases. When this happens, the diseases are classed as being autoimmune diseases.

The conditions that immunologists look at, range from hay fever and allergic reactions all the way through to cancer, leukemia & HIV. The autoimmune diseases include multiple sclerosis, rheumatoid arthritis and type I diabetes.

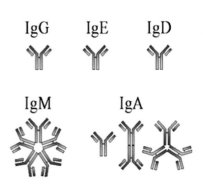

VIDEO

You can see how an allergy test is carried out and what one of the immune system's own chemicals called Histamine does to the skin in a short video. Check it out here: www.medicalmavericks.co.uk/book

What to do to get into this career...

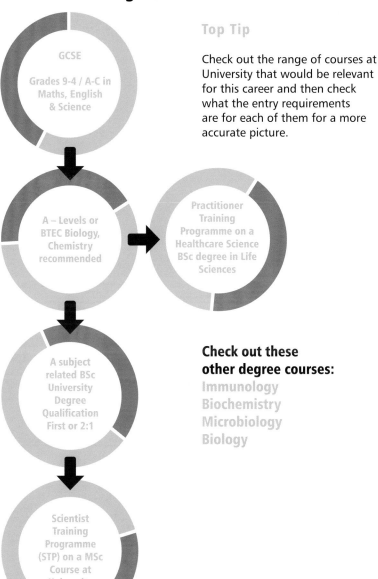

GCSE

Grades 9-4 / A-C in
Maths, English
& Science

A – Levels or
BTEC Biology,
Chemistry
recommended

Practitioner
Training
Programme on a
Healthcare Science
BSc degree in Life
Sciences

A subject
related BSc
University
Degree
Qualification
First or 2:1

Scientist
Training
Programme
(STP) on a MSc
Course at
University

Top Tip

Check out the range of courses at
University that would be relevant
for this career and then check
what the entry requirements
are for each of them for a more
accurate picture.

**Check out these
other degree courses:**
Immunology
Biochemistry
Microbiology
Biology

AMAZING FACT

The common name for cytopathology tests is a smear test. This is because the cell samples taken from a patient are smeared across a slide for analysis

Cytopathology use expensive light microscopes to detect diseases at a cellular level and can be split into two specialisms. The first is cervical cytology, which involves the examination of smear samples from cervical cancer screening. The reason for splitting cervical cytology from diagnostic, is probably due to the vast number of tests carried out under the NHS Cervical Cancer Screening Programme.

Under this scheme, over 3million women each year from the age of 25 through to 64, are screened for cervical cancer! Once qualified as a cytopathologist, it is possible to train over about 2 years to qualify and perform the smear test procedure as well.

The second specialism is diagnostic cytopathology. Again, the main focus is cancer, but the test samples have come from other parts of the body such as the throat, urinary tract and lymph nodes.

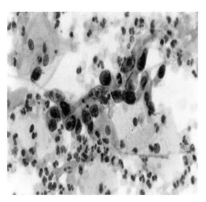

AMAZING FACT 2

Cervical screening saves around 5000 lives each year in the UK!

AMAZING FACT 3

A cytopathologist can examine cells that have come from exfoliation or aspiration. Exfoliation is when cells are taken or rubbed from the surface of a tissue in the body. Aspiration uses a needle & syringe to draw a sample of cells from a growth, tumour or lesion.

What to do to get into this career...

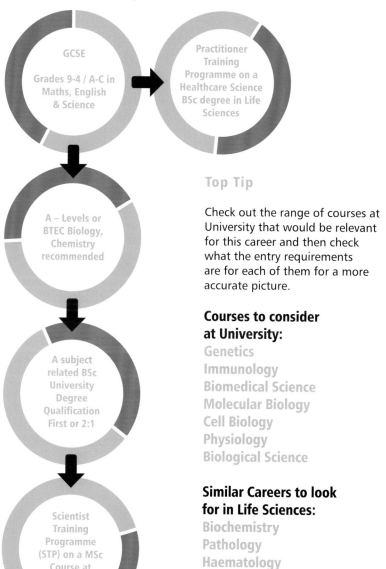

GCSE

Grades 9-4 / A-C in Maths, English & Science

Practitioner Training Programme on a Healthcare Science BSc degree in Life Sciences

A – Levels or BTEC Biology, Chemistry recommended

A subject related BSc University Degree Qualification First or 2:1

Scientist Training Programme (STP) on a MSc Course at University

Top Tip

Check out the range of courses at University that would be relevant for this career and then check what the entry requirements are for each of them for a more accurate picture.

Courses to consider at University:

Genetics
Immunology
Biomedical Science
Molecular Biology
Cell Biology
Physiology
Biological Science

Similar Careers to look for in Life Sciences:

Biochemistry
Pathology
Haematology
Clinical Immunology
Toxicology
Virology

141

AMAZING FACT

If we removed your DNA and it was stretched out it would reach to the moon 6,000 times!

These guys read the blueprints of the human body to identify any abnormal building blocks or 'genes'.

They do this by examining patients DNA samples, the blueprints. They can pick out different diseases that are inherited and are pre-programed into peoples DNA. The tests can be performed on cells from a baby before they are born, or to check if parents are carriers of a gene or to diagnose conditions, such as Downs Syndrome.

These guys where involved when Angelina Jolie was tested for the BRCA gene. A small change in this part of the massive blueprint has a 87% probability of the patient developing breast cancer. This gives the patient options and ability to have preventative surgery, just like Angelina did as she was a carrier of the altered BRCA gene.

Although these guys rarely have patient contact, they make a huge difference and are completely aware of the impacts they have on the patients and their families.

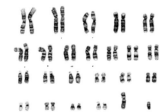

AMAZING FACT 2

With the emergence of genetics and the advancement of technology, a new sector in Healthcare Science has been created. It is called Bio-Informatics. Why has this been created? Well, as we develop a better understanding of genetics and how this relates to our health, we are going to have to store data such as an individual's genetic code… that would take a lot of paper!

What to do to get into this career...

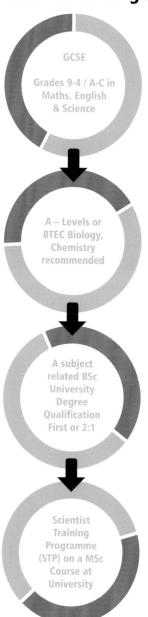

GCSE
Grades 9-4 / A-C in Maths, English & Science

A – Levels or BTEC Biology, Chemistry recommended

A subject related BSc University Degree Qualification First or 2:1

Scientist Training Programme (STP) on a MSc Course at University

Top Tip

Check out our video on Angelina Jolie and why she had a double mastectomy on our YouTube Channel – MedicalMavericksTV

Alternative courses to Consider at University:
Genetics
Biomedical Science
Microbiology

VIDEO

You can check out an interview with geneticists and see what they do in an awesome video on our website. Go to www.medicalmavericks.co.uk/book to see the video.

AMAZING FACT | The human body creates 2,500,000 new red blood cells every second

Working in the blood lab these scientists provide a vital 24/7 service in the part of diagnosing and monitoring the blood and bone marrow of patients.

A haematologist may work closely with other life science careers such as biochemistry, but the main diseases that they would be involved with include:

- Sickle cell anaemia
- Anaemia
- Leukaemia
- Haemophilia

Haematologists can also been involved in the cutting edge research into cures and new treatments for these diseases.

VIDEO

If you want to see what happens to a blood sample in a lab, check out www.medicalmavericks.co.uk/book You can watch a video on how a blood sample is taken and how it is processed to count the number of white blood cells.

What to do to get into this career...

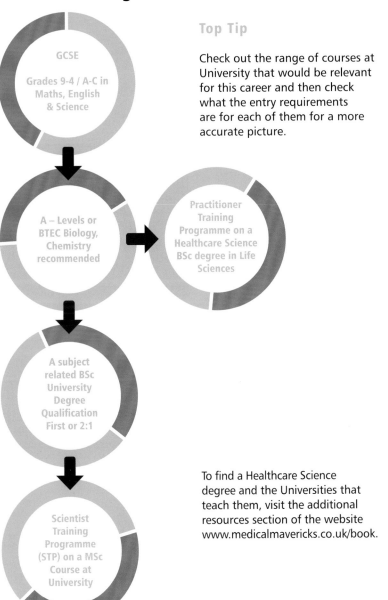

Check out the range of courses at University that would be relevant for this career and then check what the entry requirements are for each of them for a more accurate picture.

GCSE

Grades 9-4 / A-C in Maths, English & Science

A – Levels or BTEC Biology, Chemistry recommended

Practitioner Training Programme on a Healthcare Science BSc degree in Life Sciences

A subject related BSc University Degree Qualification First or 2:1

Scientist Training Programme (STP) on a MSc Course at University

To find a Healthcare Science degree and the Universities that teach them, visit the additional resources section of the website www.medicalmavericks.co.uk/book.

AMAZING FACT

These guys would have featured in Eastenders when Dexter donated his kidney to his Dad, Sam.

These guys play a really important role in organ transplant teams. They are responsible for checking if an organ donor and recipient are a match, which is crucial for a successful organ transplant.

Their place of work is within a lab and they work with tissue and cell samples from both donors and recipients. To check if there is a match, they perform a mini transplant in a dish! They mix cell samples from both patients along with antibodies and chemicals from the immune system and see if there is a reaction.

The picture on the right shows two cells from this procedure. The green cell means there is a match and the red means there would be an organ rejection!

VIDEO

You can watch an interview with a Immunogeneticist and see how they match an organ donor and organ recipient in a lab! Go to www.medicalmavericks.co.uk/book and watch the video.

What to do to get into this career...

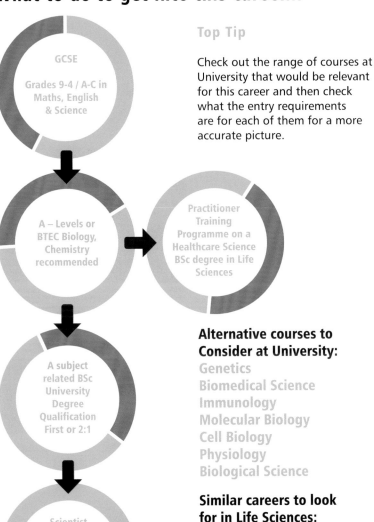

GCSE

Grades 9-4 / A-C in
Maths, English
& Science

A – Levels or
BTEC Biology,
Chemistry
recommended

Practitioner
Training
Programme on a
Healthcare Science
BSc degree in Life
Sciences

A subject
related BSc
University
Degree
Qualification
First or 2:1

Scientist
Training
Programme
(STP) on a MSc
Course at
University

Top Tip

Check out the range of courses at
University that would be relevant
for this career and then check
what the entry requirements
are for each of them for a more
accurate picture.

Alternative courses to Consider at University:

Genetics
Biomedical Science
Immunology
Molecular Biology
Cell Biology
Physiology
Biological Science

Similar careers to look for in Life Sciences:

Biochemistry
Pathology
Haematology
Clinical Immunology
Toxicology
Virology

147

Microbiologist

Area of HCS: Life Science
Pay scale: Bands 6-9 £26k - £100k

AMAZING FACT

Electron Microscopes can magnify things up to 10 million times. (Check out the house dust mite below)

Contrary to the name, this is a huge part of biology and medical research. They study microscopic organisms that can be deadly to humans such as bacteria and viruses, characterising them and developing effective treatments against diseases.

As well as bacteria, microbiologists also study:

• Viruses such as HIV
• Fungal infections such as athlete's foot
• Parasites such as tapeworm

This research enables the patients to get the best and most up-to-date treatments available. Not only do they get to use electron microscopes but they use the machine to the right to carry out PCR (polymer chain reaction), which enables them to take a tiny sample of DNA and multiply it!!

VIDEO

We've put a really cool video from Australia that looks at the day in the life of a microbiologist on our website. Check out www.medicalmavericks.co.uk/book if you want to watch it!

148

What to do to get into this career...

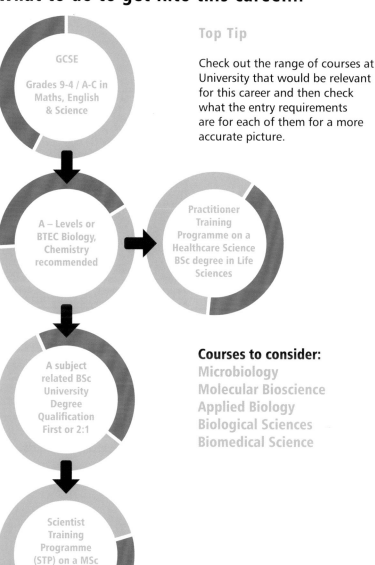

GCSE

Grades 9-4 / A-C in Maths, English & Science

A – Levels or BTEC Biology, Chemistry recommended

Practitioner Training Programme on a Healthcare Science BSc degree in Life Sciences

A subject related BSc University Degree Qualification First or 2:1

Scientist Training Programme (STP) on a MSc Course at University

Top Tip

Check out the range of courses at University that would be relevant for this career and then check what the entry requirements are for each of them for a more accurate picture.

Courses to consider:
Microbiology
Molecular Bioscience
Applied Biology
Biological Sciences
Biomedical Science

AMAZING FACT

The first baby to be born using the IVF treatment was Louise Joy Brown born 25 July 1978 at Oldham General Hospital.

As a reproductive scientist you work in the science of creating life – how amazing it that! There are two areas you can specialise in. The first area is andrology, which deals with the male reproductive system and Embryology, which is the female reproductive system.

This can be a tough job as you will work with couples that even after your help, will not be able to conceive and have children of their own. So, the emotional, communication and team working skills must be excellent.

One of the procedures you will be part of is In Vitro Fertilisation or IVF. This is a procedure to insert sperm into an egg outside of the human body. IVF is a modern technique, which provides solutions to infertility. Working with cutting edge research, reproductive scientist are striving to find better outcomes for fertility treatment.

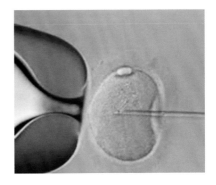

AMAZING FACT 2

One round of IVF can cost £5,000 and 1 in 5 IVF births result in multiple babies (twins or more!) compared to 1 in 80 naturally conceived babies. This is because more than one fertalised egg is implanted during the cycle.

What to do to get into this career...

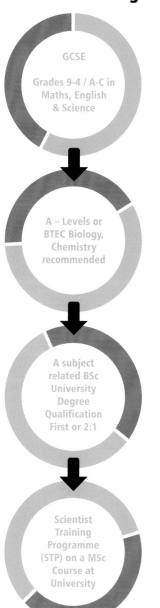

GCSE

Grades 9-4 / A-C in Maths, English & Science

A – Levels or BTEC Biology, Chemistry recommended

A subject related BSc University Degree Qualification First or 2:1

Scientist Training Programme (STP) on a MSc Course at University

Top Tip

Check out the range of courses at University that would be relevant for this career and then check what the entry requirements are for each of them for a more accurate picture.

SEARCH

A really cool website to check out if you are interested in this area is www.hfea.gov.uk This is the one stop place to go for patients and clinicians to find out more on procedures and careers.

Courses to Consider at University

Physiology
Biomedical Science
Human Biology
Biology

To find a Healthcare Science degree and the Uni's that teach them, visit the Student Zone on the Medical Mavericks website www.medicalmavericks.co.uk/book.

AMAZING FACT | Dustin Hoffman played the role of a Virologist in the 1995 film Outbreak.

If they're not filming for another monkey born virus film they are working alongside other microbiologists studying the effects and causes of viral infections.

Surprisingly, a virologist is not all lab based and they work directly with patients. This means you will have to be a good communicator, be able to listen to patient concerns and respond to any questions and concerns.

The range of diseases they are involved with range from the flu to HIV. Other viruses include:

• Rubella
• Herpes
• Hepatitis

In addition to helping treat and identify diseases, a virologist would also have a role along side other departments such as microbiology, in preventing infections in both the hospital and community.

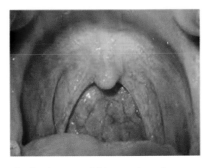

Virologists would have played a key part in the fight against the Ebola outbreak in West Africa during 2014/15 testing people with symptoms as well as other medical staff who were in contact with patients every day.

What to do to get into this career...

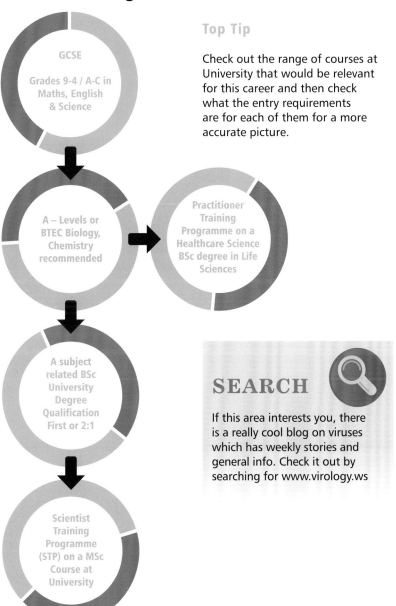

GCSE

Grades 9-4 / A-C in
Maths, English
& Science

A – Levels or
BTEC Biology,
Chemistry
recommended

Practitioner
Training
Programme on a
Healthcare Science
BSc degree in Life
Sciences

A subject
related BSc
University
Degree
Qualification
First or 2:1

Scientist
Training
Programme
(STP) on a MSc
Course at
University

Top Tip

Check out the range of courses at
University that would be relevant
for this career and then check
what the entry requirements
are for each of them for a more
accurate picture.

SEARCH

If this area interests you, there
is a really cool blog on viruses
which has weekly stories and
general info. Check it out by
searching for www.virology.ws

153

AMAZING FACT | The 1st patient successfully treated with dialysis was a 67 year old woman in 1945.

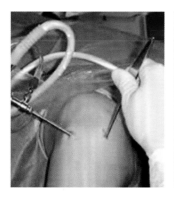

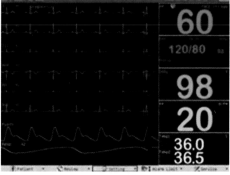

Working closely with patients, technical and medical staff, these guys design and develop modern, cutting edge equipment to help the diagnosis, treatment and rehabilitation of patients. This can be from the non-invasive keyhole surgery (as seen in our school & college workshops) to a new prosthetic that responds to muscle stimulation. They also are involved in all the monitors and kit that patients are hooked up to in hospitals to monitor their vital signs. A day could involve repairing a blood pressure machine to calibrating a piece of intensive care equipment that will keep someone alive!

HAVE YOU CONSIDERED?

You might also like to check out the Medical Engineers involved in Reconstructive Science & Rehabilitation.
You can check out these careers on the next few pages.

154

What to do to get into this career...

GCSE

Grades 9-4 / A-C in Maths, English & Science

A – Levels or BTEC Science & Technology subjects recommended

Practitioner Training Programme on a Healthcare Science BSc degree in Clinical Engineering

A subject related BSc University Degree Qualification First or 2:1

Scientist Training Programme (STP) on a MSc Course at University

Top Tip

Check out the range of courses at University that would be relevant for this career and then check what the entry requirements are for each of them for a more accurate picture.

To find a Healthcare Science degree and the Universities that teach them, visit the additional resources section of the website www.medicalmavericks.co.uk/book.

155

Clinical Pharmaceutical Scientist

Area of HCS: Clinical Engineering & Medical Physics
Pay scale: Bands 6-9 £26k - £100k

AMAZING FACT | The annual medication bill for the NHS is approx £12 Billion.

Here you get a good understanding of how drugs work and what they can be used for. This knowledge is then used in 4 main areas of pharmacy:

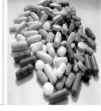

- Overseeing and maintaining areas that are used in the production and preparation of medicines, making sure the pharmacists are working in a sterile environment.

- Testing medicines to ensure they are safe and pure.

- Research and Development of new dispensing procedures of medicines.

- Preparation of radioactive substances used in various techniques.

HAVE YOU CONSIDERED?

If you are interested in how drugs work and how the body responds, you might also want to check out Analytical Toxicology on page 128. This career is all about how toxins, poisons and overdoses impact on the body and how we can treat patients who have been affected by a poison or overdose.

What to do to get into this career...

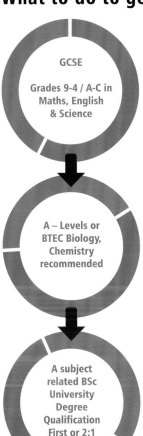

GCSE

Grades 9-4 / A-C in
Maths, English
& Science

**A – Levels or
BTEC Biology,
Chemistry
recommended**

**A subject
related BSc
University
Degree
Qualification
First or 2:1**

**Scientist
Training
Programme
(STP) on a MSc
Course at
University**

Top Tip

Check out the range of courses at
University that would be relevant
for this career and then check
what the entry requirements
are for each of them for a more
accurate picture.

Courses to Consider
at University:
**Pharmacology
Pharmaceutical Science
Immunology
Biochemistry
Medical Toxicology**

To find a Healthcare Science
degree and the Universities that
teach them, visit the additional
resources section of the website
www.medicalmavericks.co.uk/book.

Clinical Photographer

Area of HCS: Clinical Engineering & Medical Physics
Pay scale: Bands 5-7 £22k - £42k

AMAZING FACT | In a day a clinical photographer could take pictures of dead bodies, surgery wounds, bones or skin conditions to name a few!

Want the 'pic' of the jobs? Well this one is for you! Normally based in an illustration department these guys work closely with doctors and other medical staff. Although sometimes based in a hospital's clinical engineering department, from A&E to Operating Theatres. They'll take pictures of patients before and after surgery, of specific injuries, or of symptoms so doctors can record the progression of the disease and success of the treatment.

Although the role is predominantly to help future learning with giving visual aids of treatments of illnesses, you can actually be working one on one with patients to produces images that will be used in the diagnosis of a patient and for planning treatment.

VIDEO

Medical Mavericks visited a Clinical Photography department to find out more about what this department does. You can see what they do by checking out the additional resources and watching the video we made about them. Go to www.medicalmavericks.co.uk/book

158

What to do to get into this career...

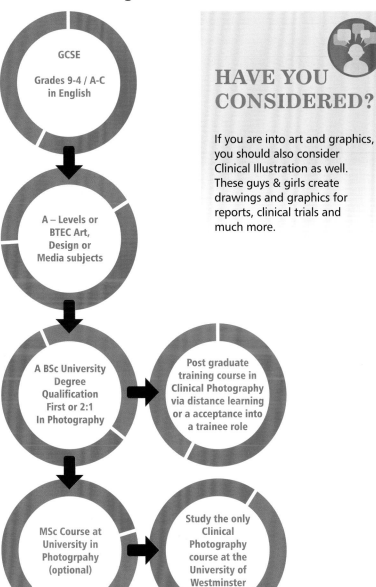

GCSE

Grades 9-4 / A-C in English

A – Levels or BTEC Art, Design or Media subjects

A BSc University Degree Qualification First or 2:1 In Photography

Post graduate training course in Clinical Photography via distance learning or a acceptance into a trainee role

MSc Course at University in Photogrpahy (optional)

Study the only Clinical Photography course at the University of Westminster

HAVE YOU CONSIDERED?

If you are into art and graphics, you should also consider Clinical Illustration as well. These guys & girls create drawings and graphics for reports, clinical trials and much more.

Clinical/Medical Technologist

Area of HCS: Clinical Engineering & Medical Physics
Pay scale: Bands 5-9 £22k - £100k

AMAZING FACT | An MRI can cost up to £6,500 per hour to run.

This area is involved in some of the most cutting-edge medical engineering, such as radiotherapy, bioengineering and laser procedures.

They can be found in a number of different departments in a hospital from; Intensive Care Units (ICU), Radiology where they prepare radioactive dye, Vascular Department where they will carry out ultrasounds, Rehabilitation team monitoring patient recovery, Renal Team working on dialysis machines to lab based research and development.

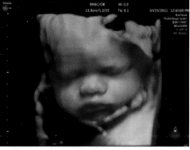

A huge array of different interests are involved in this career. Liaising with both doctors and medical staff to working with patients on a 1 to 1 basis.

HAVE YOU CONSIDERED?

There are several careers that involve the use, maintenance and creation of medical kit with this being one of them. Others to consider are Medical Engineering on page 162, Reconstructive Science on page 168 and Rehabilitation Engineering on page 170.

What to do to get into this career...

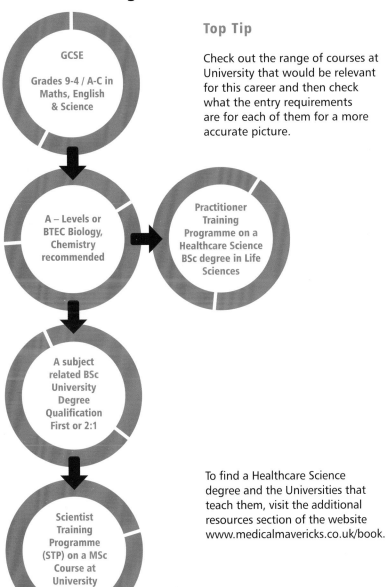

GCSE

Grades 9-4 / A-C in
Maths, English
& Science

A – Levels or
BTEC Biology,
Chemistry
recommended

Practitioner
Training
Programme on a
Healthcare Science
BSc degree in Life
Sciences

A subject
related BSc
University
Degree
Qualification
First or 2:1

Scientist
Training
Programme
(STP) on a MSc
Course at
University

Top Tip

Check out the range of courses at
University that would be relevant
for this career and then check
what the entry requirements
are for each of them for a more
accurate picture.

To find a Healthcare Science
degree and the Universities that
teach them, visit the additional
resources section of the website
www.medicalmavericks.co.uk/book.

Medical Engineer

Area of HCS: Clinical Engineering & Medical Physics
Pay Scale: Bands 5-9 £22k - £100k

AMAZING FACT

As with all HCS degrees, you spend 50 weeks of the degree course on placement in a hospital learning on the job!

To help scientists and doctors treat all patients to their best of their ability they need to use a range of equipment. Hospitals have thousands of different pieces of equipment from £10 peak flow meters, through to million pound MRI machines. It's the job of the medical engineers to keep these pieces of equipment maintained and up-to-date. If they don't have this equipment to hand patients can't get the best care available!

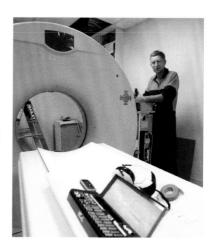

You wouldn't just be fixing equipment, you would be bringing in new kit, testing it, training people on it, maintaining it before decommissioning it at the end of it's life.

HAVE YOU CONSIDERED?

There are several careers that involve the use, maintenance and creation of medical kit with this being one of them. Others to consider are Medical Technologist on page 160, Reconstructive Science on page 168 and Rehabilitation Engineering on page 170.

What to do to get into this career...

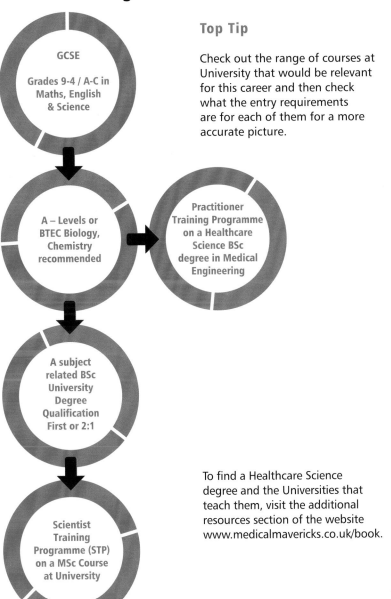

GCSE

Grades 9-4 / A-C in Maths, English & Science

A – Levels or BTEC Biology, Chemistry recommended

Practitioner Training Programme on a Healthcare Science BSc degree in Medical Engineering

A subject related BSc University Degree Qualification First or 2:1

Scientist Training Programme (STP) on a MSc Course at University

Top Tip

Check out the range of courses at University that would be relevant for this career and then check what the entry requirements are for each of them for a more accurate picture.

To find a Healthcare Science degree and the Universities that teach them, visit the additional resources section of the website www.medicalmavericks.co.uk/book.

Radiation Safety Physicist

Area of HCS: Clinical Engineering & Medical Physics
Pay scale: Bands 5-9 £22k - £100k

AMAZING FACT

The hyoid bone in your throat is the only bone in your body not attached to any other. (See below)

A key tool in treating patients is using techniques that can be used to get different images of patient from x-rays to using radioactive dyes. It's the job of these guys to make sure all the equipment and chemicals are safe for use, both for the patient and the doctor carrying out the procedure.

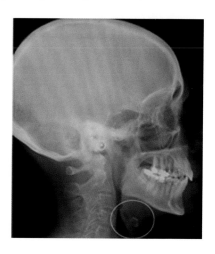

You shall work alongside a host of special areas in a hospital from acute medicine to radiology.

Techniques and research are always changing and you will have the chance to work with some of the most innovative pieces of equipment.

HAVE YOU CONSIDERED?

If you are interested in physics, imaging or even radiation, there are several other careers for you to consider. Check out Radiotherapist on page 180, Radiographer on page 180 as well as a Clinical Pharmaceutical Scientist on page 156.

What to do to get into this career...

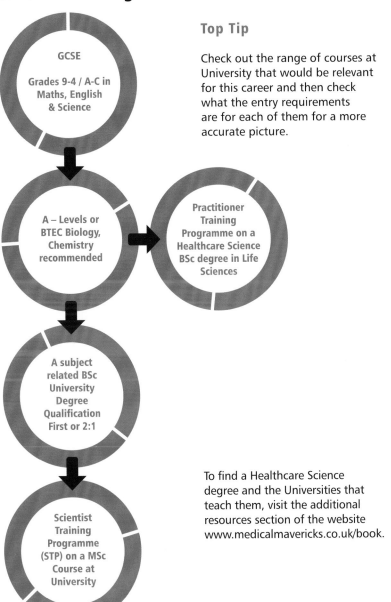

GCSE

Grades 9-4 / A-C in Maths, English & Science

A – Levels or BTEC Biology, Chemistry recommended

Practitioner Training Programme on a Healthcare Science BSc degree in Life Sciences

A subject related BSc University Degree Qualification First or 2:1

Scientist Training Programme (STP) on a MSc Course at University

Top Tip

Check out the range of courses at University that would be relevant for this career and then check what the entry requirements are for each of them for a more accurate picture.

To find a Healthcare Science degree and the Universities that teach them, visit the additional resources section of the website www.medicalmavericks.co.uk/book.

Radiotherapy Physics

Area of HCS: Clinical Engineering & Medical Physics
Pay scale: Bands 5-9 £22k - £100k

AMAZING FACT

An MRI currently under construction will produce 11.75 Teslas. The Hadron Collider, used to smash particles, creates 8.4!!

Based in the Radiology part of a hospital, they use their X-ray machines to apply high doses of radiation to a patient's body with high precision. They repeat this over a number of weeks in the hope of treating cancer cells. Before they start this treatment they have to carry out a number of other tests such as MRI and CT scans, this gives them the correct area to concentrate on therefore hopefully reducing the possibility of damaging any healthy tissue surrounding the tumour.

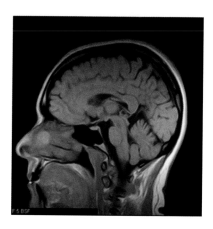

HAVE YOU CONSIDERED?

If you are interested in physics, imaging or even radiation, there are several other careers for you to consider. Check out Radiotherapist on page 180, Radiographer on page 180 as well as a Radiation Safety Physicist on page 164.

What to do to get into this career...

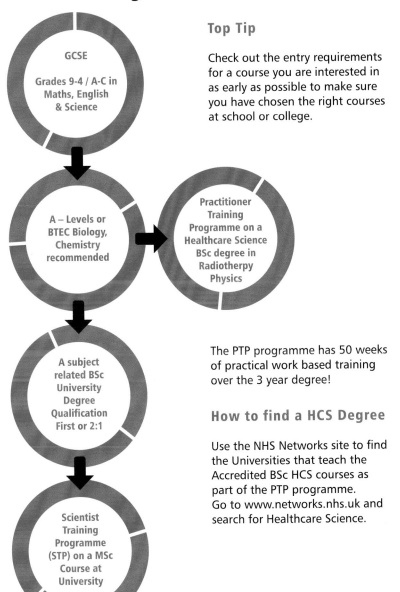

GCSE

Grades 9-4 / A-C in Maths, English & Science

A – Levels or BTEC Biology, Chemistry recommended

Practitioner Training Programme on a Healthcare Science BSc degree in Radiotherpy Physics

A subject related BSc University Degree Qualification First or 2:1

Scientist Training Programme (STP) on a MSc Course at University

Top Tip

Check out the entry requirements for a course you are interested in as early as possible to make sure you have chosen the right courses at school or college.

The PTP programme has 50 weeks of practical work based training over the 3 year degree!

How to find a HCS Degree

Use the NHS Networks site to find the Universities that teach the Accredited BSc HCS courses as part of the PTP programme. Go to www.networks.nhs.uk and search for Healthcare Science.

Reconstructive Science

Area of HCS: Clinical Engineering & Medical Physics
Pay Scale: Bands 5-9 £22k - £100k

AMAZING FACT

The 1st written account of an artificial limb was made around 500 B.C., Herodotus wrote of a prisoner who escaped from his chains by cutting off his foot, which he later replaced with a wooden substitute

A varied job that uses materials such as plastics, clay or wax to help mould and design custom made devices for patients. These could include splints, implantable skull plates made of titanium or even teeth! The patients you work with could have sustained injuries that result in a disability or disfigurement or they could have been born with malformations that need a custom made device.

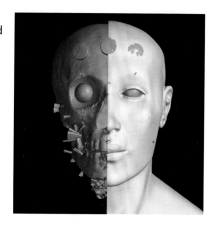

Once the treatment has been carried out, these guys are part of the on going care of the patient to make sure the treatment is the best, most up-to-date for the individual patient.

HAVE YOU CONSIDERED?

If you are interested in design and engineering, check out Rehabilitation Engineering on page 170, Clinical Engineering on page 154 and Medical Engineering on page 162.

What to do to get into this career...

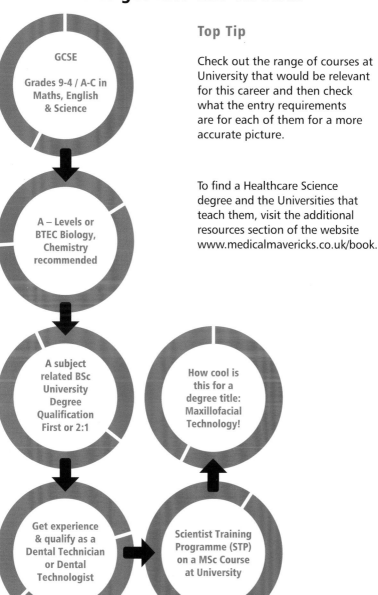

GCSE

Grades 9-4 / A-C in Maths, English & Science

A – Levels or BTEC Biology, Chemistry recommended

A subject related BSc University Degree Qualification First or 2:1

How cool is this for a degree title: Maxillofacial Technology!

Get experience & qualify as a Dental Technician or Dental Technologist

Scientist Training Programme (STP) on a MSc Course at University

Top Tip

Check out the range of courses at University that would be relevant for this career and then check what the entry requirements are for each of them for a more accurate picture.

To find a Healthcare Science degree and the Universities that teach them, visit the additional resources section of the website www.medicalmavericks.co.uk/book.

169

Rehabilitation Engineer

Area of HCS: Life Science
Pay scale: Bands 5-9 £22k - £100k

AMAZING FACT | Stephen Hawkins Voice, "Speech Synthesizer," was developed in the 1980's, it's still the original and there is only one copy!!

These guys are involved in the development of technology which match the needs of their patient.

They also are involved in making custom-made technology such as; artificial limbs, speech synthesizers, wheel chairs and robotic aids.

The latest 'bionic arm' designed by rehab engineers has allowed a man to feel the shape or softness of objects for the first time in 9 years since he lost his arm! The next step is to make the electronics smaller and smaller so they are more portable and usable by the patients.

HAVE YOU CONSIDERED?

If you are interested in design and engineering, check out Reconstructive Science on page 168, Clinical Engineering on page 154 and Medical Engineering on page 162.

What to do to get into this career...

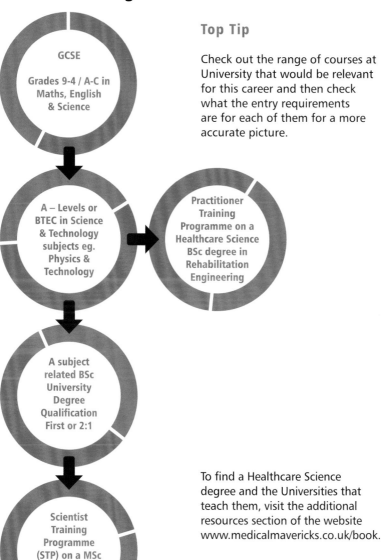

GCSE

Grades 9-4 / A-C in Maths, English & Science

A – Levels or BTEC in Science & Technology subjects eg. Physics & Technology

Practitioner Training Programme on a Healthcare Science BSc degree in Rehabilitation Engineering

A subject related BSc University Degree Qualification First or 2:1

Scientist Training Programme (STP) on a MSc Course at University

Top Tip

Check out the range of courses at University that would be relevant for this career and then check what the entry requirements are for each of them for a more accurate picture.

To find a Healthcare Science degree and the Universities that teach them, visit the additional resources section of the website www.medicalmavericks.co.uk/book.

AMAZING FACT

It's not all about food! These guys & gals work on areas such as psychology, sociology & education.

You seriously have to be a people person for this career. You also have to be a good motivator, listener and be able to explain things to your patients clearly so they can make changes to their diet and lifestyles.

As a dietician you could be working with the general public giving health & diet talks or working one on one with a patient to provide a personalised diet plan.

And it's not all about losing weight either. A patient's diet can impact on recovery from surgery, or it could be to avoid allergies to different foods, help manage eating disorders or manage conditions such as diabetes.

Some dieticians work with stats and numbers to provide advice to government and organisations on the benefits & safety of different foods in society.

AMAZING FACT 2

You can survive for around 2 months without food but only 3-5 days without water!

What to do to get into this career...

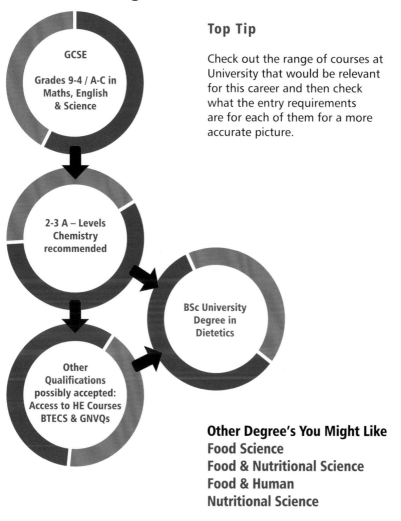

GCSE

Grades 9-4 / A-C in Maths, English & Science

2-3 A – Levels Chemistry recommended

BSc University Degree in Dietetics

Other Qualifications possibly accepted: Access to HE Courses BTECS & GNVQs

Top Tip

Check out the range of courses at University that would be relevant for this career and then check what the entry requirements are for each of them for a more accurate picture.

Other Degree's You Might Like
Food Science
Food & Nutritional Science
Food & Human
Nutritional Science

Maxillofacial Prosthetist

Pay Scale: Bands 5-9 £22k - £100k

AMAZING FACT

There are 14 bones in the face and 43 muscles. Some people have fewer facial muscles, around 40% less in some cases.

Sounds like a bit of a mouthful but these surgeons are exceptional at giving patients with disfigurement the confidence to live a normal life. They specialise in working with patients who require reconstructive work due to burns or cancer.

Their day to day work involves meeting patients taking moulds of the wound that they shall reconstruct and make sure the patient knows exactly what the procedure shall involve and how long it will take.

After the procedure it is also their job to book in follow up appointments to make sure all has gone as planned.

The top right image is of a gentlemen who has had a tumour removed and left him with no occipital cavity. The bottom image is the complete reconstruction work of a Maxillofacial Prosthetist! Simply Awesome!!

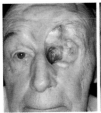
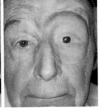

SEARCH

A really cool website to search is the Institute of Maxillofacial Prosthetists & Technologists. You can find it at www.impt.co.uk. There is a patient section where you can find out more about the types of procedures and what an MXP actually does.

What to do to get into this career...

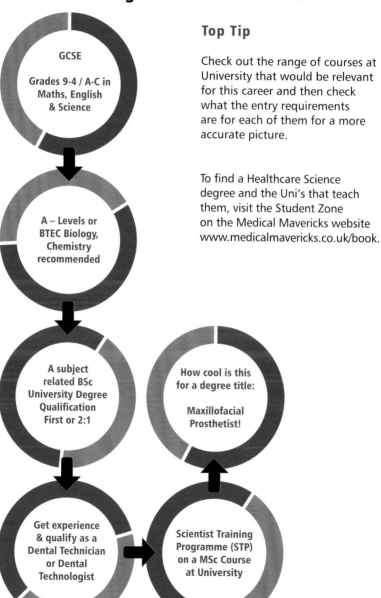

GCSE

Grades 9-4 / A-C in Maths, English & Science

A – Levels or BTEC Biology, Chemistry recommended

A subject related BSc University Degree Qualification First or 2:1

How cool is this for a degree title:

Maxillofacial Prosthetist!

Get experience & qualify as a Dental Technician or Dental Technologist

Scientist Training Programme (STP) on a MSc Course at University

Top Tip

Check out the range of courses at University that would be relevant for this career and then check what the entry requirements are for each of them for a more accurate picture.

To find a Healthcare Science degree and the Uni's that teach them, visit the Student Zone on the Medical Mavericks website www.medicalmavericks.co.uk/book.

AMAZING FACT | Occupational Therapists help people every single day recover from injury & disability. It's not all physical either, psychology and behaviours of patients are also treated.

When I first heard of an Occupational Therapist, I thought they just sat at a desk all day asking questions to get people back to work. How wrong that was!

They work in kinds of settings from hospitals, to community clinics, GP surgeries & even people's homes. It's not all about getting people back into work either. One of their biggest aims is to give patients their independence back after surgery, illness, disease or accident.

They would also work with so many different types of people from young to old, which makes the job so interesting but also calls for many different skills in communication, patience & enthusiasm.

SEARCH

If you want even more info on this career, you can check out the British Association of Occupational Therapists. Visit their website here www.cot.co.uk

What to do to get into this career...

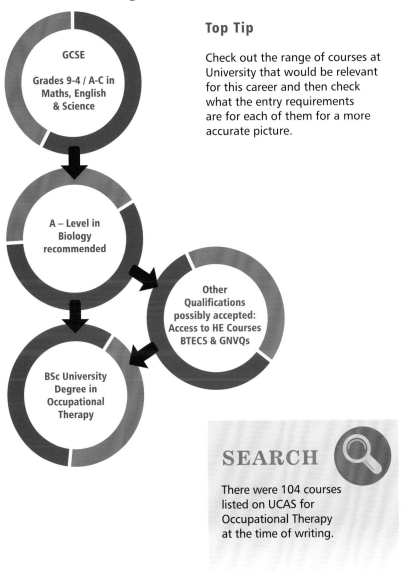

GCSE

Grades 9-4 / A-C in Maths, English & Science

A – Level in Biology recommended

Other Qualifications possibly accepted: Access to HE Courses BTECS & GNVQs

BSc University Degree in Occupational Therapy

Top Tip

Check out the range of courses at University that would be relevant for this career and then check what the entry requirements are for each of them for a more accurate picture.

SEARCH

There were 104 courses listed on UCAS for Occupational Therapy at the time of writing.

AMAZING FACT

There are four types of Glaucoma which is commonly characterised by having high fluid pressure inside the eye ball!

Working closely with other specialists in the NHS, orthoptists are critical at diagnosing conditions that effect peoples vision like; glaucoma, a range of disorders normally linked to increase in pressure inside the eye, cataract, where the lens steams up from inside, retinal disease, damage to the back of the eye and even a stroke, when the area of the brain that controls your vision is starved of oxygen.

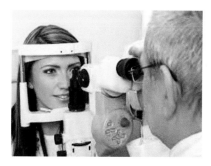

Their job doesn't stop there, they then help manage the conditions caused by these various illnesses and problems.

Orthoptists don't just work within a hospital they can go into schools to examine children, charities, private clinics, universities and specialised eye hospitals.

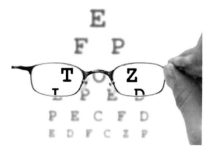

SEARCH

You can find even more details on Orthoptics by going to the British & Irish Orthoptics Society. Check them out here – www.orthoptics.org.uk They are even on Twitter - @FollowBios

What to do to get into this career...

5 GCSEs

Grades 9-4 / A-C in Maths, English & Science

Other Qualifications possibly accepted: Access to HE Courses BTECS & GNVQs + 1 A Level

3 year course at University BSc Hon in Orthoptics

Top Tip

There are only 3 universities that teach Orthoptics. These are Liverpool, Sheffield and Glasgow Caledonian.

HAVE YOU CONSIDERED?

If you are interested in the eyes why not check out Ophthalmic & Vision Science. It is a Healthcare Science career and can be found on page 120.

To find a Healthcare Science degree and the Universities that teach them, visit the additional resources section of the website www.medicalmavericks.co.uk/book.

AMAZING FACT

There are around 26,000 diagnostic radiographers in the UK and you spend 50% of your time when training in a hospital, learning on the job!

The most common machine and test a Diagnostic Radiographer will use is an X-Ray machine. But you may not know they are also trained to use the following bits of kit:

- Fluoroscopy. This allows them to image the digestive system
- CT Scan to provide cross sectional images of the body
- MRI scans to create 3D images
- Ultrasound to image organs quickly and check circulation

They work with many departments from A&E, to critical care and normal wards. When training, one of the main subjects you will study is Anatomy, which is the study of the structures in the body.

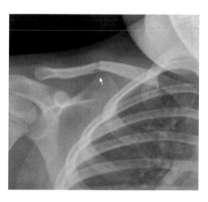

This is Tom's daughter's X-ray from when she broke her collarbone. She slipped on her Disney princess dress and fell down the stairs! Check out more X-rays on the free resources section of the website.
www.medicalmavericks.co.uk/book

HAVE YOU CONSIDERED?

There are two types of Radiography, Diagnostic and Therapeutic. Therapeutic Radiographers treat cancer patients with different types of radiation treatment. Check this career out as well as the Diagnostic type.

What to do to get into this career...

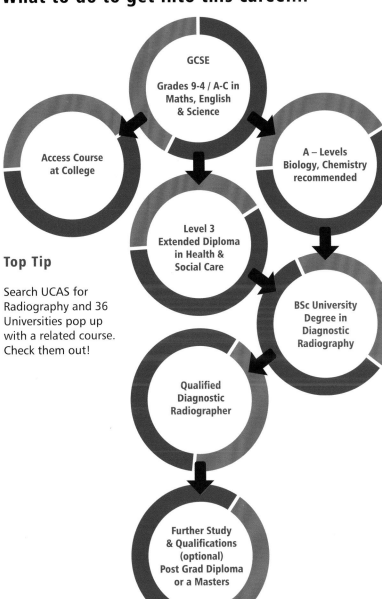

GCSE
Grades 9-4 / A-C in Maths, English & Science

Access Course at College

A – Levels Biology, Chemistry recommended

Level 3 Extended Diploma in Health & Social Care

BSc University Degree in Diagnostic Radiography

Qualified Diagnostic Radiographer

Further Study & Qualifications (optional) Post Grad Diploma or a Masters

Top Tip

Search UCAS for Radiography and 36 Universities pop up with a related course. Check them out!

Speech & Language Therapist

Pay Scale: Bands 5-7 £22k - £42k

AMAZING FACT

The Hyoid bone at the top of the neck, just above the trachea, helps us move our tongue and is not connected to any other bones in the body.

This is one seriously cool career that uses so many areas of science and physiology. You see, SLT involves knowing about muscles in the head and throat, biomechanics, hearing, how the brain interprets words.

Working all over the hospital, from stroke wards to outpatients, they also work directly with patients in their own homes or nursing homes.

Problems with swallowing or communication due to a stroke or Parkinson's disease for example as two of the main issues patients require help with.

In the UK one of the biggest issues for this career over the last few decades has been working with ethnic minorities. Nowadays speech therapists are trying to work in their patient's native language and even use computer software to help communicate.

HAVE YOU CONSIDERED?

If you are into speech and sounds you could also check out Audiology, which is a healthcare science career and can be found on page 108. Or if you are into design and art, why not check out a Maxillofacial Prosthetist on page 174.

What to do to get into this career...

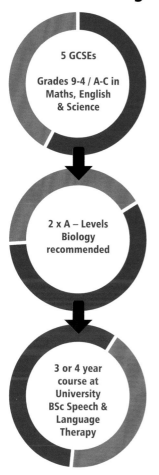

5 GCSEs

Grades 9-4 / A-C in
Maths, English
& Science

2 x A – Levels
Biology
recommended

3 or 4 year
course at
University
BSc Speech &
Language
Therapy

Top Tip

Check out the range of courses at
University that would be relevant
for this career and then check
what the entry requirements
are for each of them for a more
accurate picture.

SEARCH

At the time of writing
there were 26 Universities
that provided a Speech &
Language Therapy Course.
Check them out by searching
UCAS for Speech and
Language Therapy.
www.ucas.ac.uk

AMAZING FACT

You get to work with a surgery team and go into surgery. Yes, you read that right, YOU GET TO GO INTO SURGERY!!!

An ODP is part of the operating team and work in surgical theatres. They work with patients in the anaesthetic phase, surgical phase and recovery phase. There are load of different jobs they can do from infection control to passing the surgical instruments to the surgeon. This means you have to count the instruments out and then count them back in – don't leave them in the patient!

After surgery an ODP can be involved in wound care, making sure the patient is recovering well and there is no risk of infection. This is such an important role and they have to work as part of a wide clinical team.

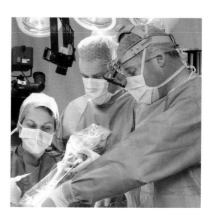

AMAZING FACT 2

At the time of writing you could study for 2 years and qualify with a Diploma in Higher Education or study for 3 years for a Bachelor of Science Degree.

HAVE YOU CONSIDERED?

An ODP is heavily involved with patient care throughout surgery, so if working with patients is something you are really interested in, you should check out all of the Physiology careers as well. They can be found from page 108.

What to do to get into this career...

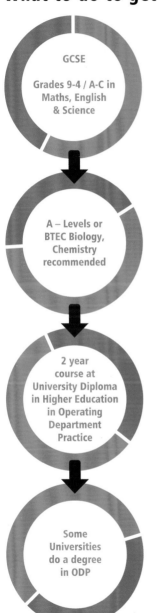

GCSE

Grades 9-4 / A-C in Maths, English & Science

A – Levels or BTEC Biology, Chemistry recommended

2 year course at University Diploma in Higher Education in Operating Department Practice

Some Universities do a degree in ODP

Top Tip

Check out the range of courses at University that would be relevant for this career and then check what the entry requirements are for each of them for a more accurate picture.

Some students can get their tuition fees paid for, get a £1,000 grant and apply for a £4,395 means-tested bursary if they are eligible. To find out more go to **www.nhsbsa.nhs.uk/nhs-bursary-students**

To find out where to study you can also check out this great course finder on the NHS Careers website **www.healthcareers.nhs.uk**

SEARCH

Check out www.copd.org.uk to find ODP courses and more in depth info on this career.

185

AMAZING FACT

When you start your training you actually go out on the road with qualified paramedics in your 1st year!!!

Many medical careers can have a routine and a set of conditions that they deal with each day. As a paramedic, you never know what condition or who you will be treating next. As the first on the scene, the decisions you make about the treatments you need to give the patient could be the difference between life and death.

One minute you could be dealing with an allergic reaction in a child, the next a heart attack in an elderly person. How would you respond to a road traffic accident or a stabbing?

SEARCH

Search UCAS for Paramedic and you will find 40 Universities offering this as a course.

This career needs you to be switched on at all times, be able to make decisions quickly, and most of all, make sure your patients understand what is happening and are safe at all times.

SEARCH

Check out the College of Paramedics that has loads of info on this career as well as guidance for when you actually become one! Visit www.collegeofparamedics.co.uk to find out more.

What to do to get into this career...

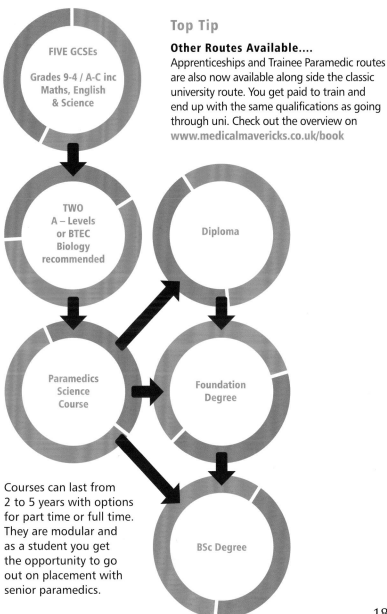

FIVE GCSEs

Grades 9-4 / A-C inc
Maths, English
& Science

TWO
A – Levels
or BTEC
Biology
recommended

Diploma

Paramedics
Science
Course

Foundation
Degree

BSc Degree

Top Tip

Other Routes Available....
Apprenticeships and Trainee Paramedic routes
are also now available along side the classic
university route. You get paid to train and
end up with the same qualifications as going
through uni. Check out the overview on
www.medicalmavericks.co.uk/book

Courses can last from
2 to 5 years with options
for part time or full time.
They are modular and
as a student you get
the opportunity to go
out on placement with
senior paramedics.

187

Chapter 16

The Other NHS Sectors

As well as Healthcare Science the Allied Health Professions covered in this book, there are many more sectors in the NHS that you might want to go and explore.

Luckily for you, we've put a quick over view in here! These sections include careers that work in offices, in catering, gardening, architecture as well as loads of other medical based careers. Some work with patients, some work behind the scenes!

Each sector has a brief overview of what you need at GCSE, what you need to do at Uni (if that is needed), some top tips and lists of career titles to explore further.

You can find the ultimate guide for all these sectors on the NHS careers website. Do the following to find out more:

- Visit www.healthcareers.nhs.uk
- Click Explore Roles at the top of the page
- This lists all the sectors
- You can click them to expand the boxes on the site and go into each career in turn to find out more

Have a look through the following pages to find out more and see what you can discover!

1. Healthcare Science

GCSE: 5 x Levels 9-4. Eng, Maths & Sci are important.

University? University Degree.

40+ careers to choose from.

Some have patient contact, some don't.

Specialisms include:
- Physiology
- Lab Science
- Medical Engineering
- Medical Physics

Consider this if you like all the sciences or engineering, IT, Technology, Electronics.

2. Nursing

GCSE: 5 x Levels 9-4. Eng, Maths & Sci are important.

University? University Degree.

Lots of Unis have two course intakes each year – Sept & April.

Work with patients & pretty much every other career in a hospital.

See loads of different things! Surgery, medicines, treatments, death, babies, kids, adults.

Lots of areas to choose from:
- Adult
- Child
- Learning Disability
- Mental Health

More specialisms later on after qualifying.

3. Midwifery

GCSE: 5 x Levels 9-4. Eng, Maths & Sci are important.

University? Degree in Midwifery.

Work in hospital & Community.

Main role is to monitor unborn baby and Mom!

Alternate Route In

If you don't get in 1st time. Go away, get some healthcare work experience and re-apply when you are a little older / more mature!

You can become and Nurse and then do a 78 week training course to become a Midwife!

4. Management

GCSE: 5 x A-C / 9-4

University? Various degrees – Business, Management, IT.

Virtually no patient contact.

More office based.

Work behind the scenes to make sure hospital runs as smoothly as possible.

Specialisms include:
- Finance
- Human Resources
- Sterilisation & decontamination
- General Management

Consider this if you don't fancy blood and science!

5. Physician Associate

GCSE: 5 x A-C / 9-5

University? You need a science degree 1st, then study a postgraduate top up.

Relatively new career in the NHS.

Good option if you don't get into medicine.

Work closely with patients.

Support Doctors in diagnosing & managing patients.

Consider this if you like medical careers but want to keep your options open at Uni.

6. Medicine

GCSE: A & A* / 7-9 levels. You need Chemistry @ A-Level!

University? Basic – 5 years of uni med school, 2 years as Junior Doctor.

About 1/3 get an interview

50% get an offer after interview

Get lots of life experience! Join clubs, get a part time job, meet people!

Work Experience Tip: Think outside the box. Go to other medical industries like biomedical engineering, pharmacy, prosthetics, lab based careers. The Unis will love it!

7. Dentistry

GCSE: A & B / 6-9 level. A-levels are more important!

University? You need Chemistry 5 year University course.

Work with patients.

You have to complete an Aptitude Test to gain entry too.

You can do a pre-dental year if you don't have science qualifications!

Other Dental careers include:
- Dental Hygenist
- Dental Technician
- Dental Nurse
- Dental Therapist

These have lower entry standard and multiple entry routes.

8. Health Informatics

GCSE: A-C / 9-4 Maths, English and IT are important.

University? Various routes. Some University some Apprentice & on the job training.

Uni courses to consider: IT, Technology, Maths & Stats.

This area allows the NHS to get information as efficiently as possible.

Some work with paper based records, some involve getting electronic records and others are involved in the developing systems & programs to store and distribute information.

Specialisms include:
- Coders
- ICT technicians
- Health Records
- Librarians
- IT Trainers
- Clerks

9. Ambulance Service

GCSE: A-C / 9-4 levels. Maths, English & Science.

University? 3 year Paramedic Science Degree.

As well as University routes you can become a student paramedic. It takes longer but you get paid to train. Places are limited too.

Driving is a key skill.

There are other roles too that support the paramedics on the road:
- Call Handler (answering 999)
- Emergency Dispatch
- Ambulance Care Assistant
- Patient Transport

Consider this if you want to work in a close knit team and be at the forefront of the action!

10. Allied Health Professions

GCSE: Some A-C / 9-4, some A-B / 9-6.

University? Various courses depending on career path.

One of THE most varied parts of the NHS and mainly work directly with patients.

Career choices include:
- Occupational Therapist
- Physiotherapy
- Podiatrist (feet!)
- Dietician
- Arts, Drama & Music Therapist
- Psychologist
- Speech & Language Therapist
- Radiographer
- Operating Department Practitioner

There is something for everyone here!

194

11. Wider Healthcare Team

GCSE: Varied, typically A-C incl Maths & English.

University? Varied: Some do, some don't.

Just like the Allied Professions, this a real mix of different careers.

These help the NHS run like clock work.

Careers include:

- Architect
- Drivers
- Maintenance
- Receptionists
- Medical Secretary
- Catering
- Health Promotion Staff
- Porters
- Personal Assistants
- And many more!

To find out more about these amazing careers you can visit:

www.medicalmavericks.co.uk/student-zone

or visit the NHS careers website:

www.healthcareers.nhs.uk
and click the explore roles link
at the top of the page.

EVEN MORE AWESOME RESOURCES & WORKSHOPS!!!

We can visit your school, college or event with our amazing **REAL HOSPITAL** and **MOBILE SPORTS SCIENCE LAB**. **Turn the page to find out more.**

Pages 200 to 211
Medical Workshops & Activities

Pages 212 to 217
Sports Science Workshops & Activities

WHAT WE DO

	Shows	**Medical Workshops**
What	The Human Guinea Pig Show	Careers in Health or Health MOT or Mini Medics
Who	Year 9 and up!	Primary: Years 4-6 Sec & College: Years 7 - 13
How	2 – 3 shows in a day to as many students as you can fit into your hall! This amazing show introduces amazing careers in the NHS that require levels 9-4 at GCSE in maths, english & science with live demos & fascinating video footage or real medical procedures!	5 – 6 workshops repeated inline with your timetable for 30-40 students or 2 – 3 longer workshops for up to 60 students. Hands on activities where your students get to use real medical kit in the classroom including ultrasound machines, ECGs, keyhole surgery & so much more!
Where	Page 200	Page 201, 202 & 203

The Quickie Guide

	Sports Science Workshops	Super Science Day
What	Challenge the Champions or Sports Hall Science PLUS	Custom day that mixes everything!
Who	Primary: Years 4-6 Sec & College: Years 7 - 13	Primary: Years 4-6 Sec & College: Years 7 - 13
How	5 – 6 workshops repeated inline with your timetable for 30-40 students or 2 – 3 longer workshops for up to 60 students. Hands on activities where your students get to complete amazing sports science tests to compare themselves to some of the world's best athletes... even racing a virtual Usain Bolt!	Engage & inspire a whole year group or a select group of students for the day! Kick of with a show and then rotate the students around a carousel of workshops that mix medicine, health and sports science. Loads of STEM careers and curriculum links!
Where	Pages 212 – 217	Look at everything!!

The Human Guinea Pig Show

Who is it for?
Ideally suited for year 9 and up

How many can take part?
As many as you can fit into your hall! We usually repeat the show 2-3 times over the day

How long is it?
Minimum 50 minutes, max 70 minutes.

Tom as his alter ego - The Human Guinea Pig.

What is it?
This is a fantastic live science stage show, where Tom takes your students on a journey through different NHS departments that he has visited. He shows them some amazing video footage of the medical procedures he has gone through... just for the fun of it! Tom also invites willing volunteers up on stage to become mini human guinea pigs with some live medical tests on stage!!!!

How does it help you?
This is all about careers and STEM. The show is a great way to showcase medical based careers to your students that don't need A & A* grades, making them accessible to A-C grade students.

Tom doing his 'thang' at the Big Bang Fair North West.

As used by

The **Big Bang**
UK Young Scientists & Engineers Fair

BRITISH SCIENCE ASSOCIATION

Careers in Health Workshop

Who is it for?
Ideally suited for year 9-13 and Access Courses

How many can take part?
30 – 40 per workshop

How long is it?
50-70 minutes, repeated over the day
to different groups.

Chris and Greg helping
Eddy the Head breathe.

What is it?
It is an amazing hands on workshop where your pupils get to use real medical kit in the classroom to discover a range of careers in the NHS they never knew existed along side the most popular choices such as nursing and medicine. Activities include: taking blood from a fake arm using a real needle, using an ultrasound machine to see inside their body, trying key hole surgery, scanning the retina in their eye with an iPhone and much more!

How does it help you?
This is all about careers and STEM. The workshop is a great way to showcase medical based careers to your students that don't need A & A* grades, making them accessible to A-C grade students. **Most importantly it helps the school evidence the provision of impartial and informed careers advice.**

Tom showing Amy her heart on the ultrasound machine

That's your heart on the screen!

201

Health MOT Workshop

Who is it for?
Ideally suited for years 7, 8 & 9

How many can take part?
30 – 40 per workshop

How long is it?
50-70 minutes, repeated over the day
to different groups. .

Craig testing his Carbon
Monoxide levels... he passed
and was not a smoker!

What is it?
A hands on workshop where we link the medical to kit to health themes such as smoking, obesity, healthy diet, heart disease, strokes & ageing. Activities include, lung function tests, carbon monoxide tests, recording ECGs from their heart, scanning blood vessels in their eye and experiencing ageing with our ageing suit.

How does it help you?
Health education and PSHE is a tough one to teach. It isn't your specialist subject and organising a day on these themes just adds to your workload. This is a pre-prepared workshop that links in with key PSHE health themes. All you have to do is book us, book a room and bring the students along.

Jas, Kimi, Kurdeep & Mas experiencing different eye diseases with our pathology goggles.

202

Mini Medics Workshop

Who is it for?
G & T pupils, BTEC, A-level or IBAC students

How many can take part?
40 – 50 per workshop

How long is it?
Minimum 2 hours, max full day.
(Can be repeated over the day)

Chig getting the ultrasound machine ready.

What is it?
This is a more in depth workshop that can be linked to curriculum specs for BTEC and A-level as well as having the careers links. They use all the fantastic kit from Careers in Health along side additional activities such as suturing fake skin, recording respiration rates and taking measurements on the size of their blood vessels using the ultrasound machine!

How does it help you?
If you teach BTEC this workshop will help you evidence units that require Physiological measurement in one go! There is some much data to collect from respiration rates to blood vessel dimensions. **If you have a G&T group or a high achievers group**, this workshop can help inspire them further with some really advanced tests!

Charlotte & Jane taking blood from Andy the injection arm!

Ultrasound Machines

Tom showing Chig his elbow joint on the ultrasound machine.

Activity

Students can use the ultrasound machine to see inside their own body! There are two probes; a flat and a curved. We use these in different workshops, but your students will be able to see the following:

- Bones, muscles, tendons (flat)
- Growth plates in their long bones!! (flat)
- Blood vessels including Aorta, Vena Cava, Carotid (flat and curved)
- Heart, liver, kidneys (curved)

They can also take measurements of blood flow speed and blood vessel dimensions such as diameter, circumference and area!

Careers Links
- Sonographer
- Radiographer
- Cardiac Physiologist
- Vascular Scientist

Health Links
- Heart Disease
- Liver Failure
- Osteoporosis
- Sports Injuries

To book call (01902) 595 060
Or email hello@medicalmavericks.co.uk

204

iPhone Retina Scan

That's your retina & optic disc on the screen!

Tom, scanning Jackie's retina & optic disc with the iPhone Ophthalmoscope.

Activity
Using a special bracket, we can attach an iPhone 4 to an Ophthalmoscope and take a picture of the optic disc and blood vessels in the retina!

This piece of kit is a great example of many different careers coming together to speed up diagnosis & treatments of patients with eye conditions and making it more accessible so we can treat more people in a shorter space of time!

Careers Links
- Ophthalmic Scientist
- Optician
- Medical Engineer
- Software Developer

Health Links
- Diabetes
- High Blood Pressure
- Glaucoma
- Blindness

"Yep, we can take a picture of the inside of your eye... on an iPhone... get it... EYE – PHONE. (I'll get my coat). This is one of the most popular activities. You can even tweet, email or post the picture to facebook & twitter straight from the phone!"

MEDICAL MAVERICKS

TOM SAYS

MEDICAL MAVERICKS

To book call (01902) 595 060
Or email hello@medicalmavericks.co.uk

Recording & Printing an ECG

Dan examining Dave's ECG on the computer with Alex looking over it too.

Activity

Everybody recognises the wavy line you see at the start of Holby City... but don't always know what it is called. During the workshop your students get to record their very own ECG, or Electrocardiogram.

It is a simple ECG from a 3 lead set up where the students put sticky electrodes on their wrists and elbow. They even get to print it off too!

Careers Links

- Cardiac Physiologist
- Doctor
- Paramedic
- Nurse

Health Links

- Heart Disease
- Obesity

"Don't worry... we've never had any flat liners before! Student love to see their heart beat on the screen and even experiment to see what happens when they hold their breath or do some exercise."

To book call (01902) 595 060
Or email hello@medicalmavericks.co.uk

Take blood from Andy!

Activity

OK, first things first... the blood is fake and Andy is not a real person! He is a phlebotomy training arm (a fake arm with fake blood vessels!) BUT your students do get to use a real needle to take a blood sample from, Andy and even examine cannulas.

Careers Links

There are so many careers that link to this activities from Nursing, to Paramedics to Phlebotomy to Medicine.

"This is totally safe and fully supervised at all times. Students love the fact they are using a real needle and are fascinated by how it works."

Dawn showing her friends how to take blood from Andy the injection arm.

To book call (01902) 595 060
Or email hello@medicalmavericks.co.uk

207

Try Key Hole Surgery

Harry trying complete the key hole surgery challenge with Jaz and Nick helping out.

Activity

You didn't think surgeons are just let loose on patients willy-nilly did you? They have to practice and this is how they do it! Using a what looks like a white brief case your students have to put the surgical instruments through the holes and complete a series of tasks from stretching elastic bands around pegs or threading a shoe lace through holes. They get to see what is going on inside the box via a camera and computer screen.

Careers Links
- Surgeon
- Physiotherapist
- Operating Department Practitioner

Health Links
- Sports Injuries
- Obesity
- Heart Failure
- Appendicitis

"Some students find this soooo frustrating, where as others find it easy as 1,2,3. You did get to see student's concentration faces though, when taking part in this activity. Gamers are especially good at this task."

To book call (01902) 595 060
Or email hello@medicalmavericks.co.uk

Suture & Stitch Fake Skin

Activity

As well as the key hole surgery we let some groups of students have a go at putting stitches in to some fake skin. They can even use a special frame to place their mobile phone on and video the whole thing. The biggest problem students have is using both hands to complete the task in a coordinated way.

The use of mobiles to view what they are doing is very important. Surgeons are completing more and more surgery via screens and remote equipment, that they have to get used to viewing their activities on a 2D screen instead of their own normal 3D vision.

Careers Links

- Surgeon
- Operating Department Practitioner
- Physiotherapist

Health Links

- Sports Injuries
- Obesity
- Heart Failure

Sue recording her suturing skills on her mobile phone.

"I can't sew to save my life... never mind doing this on fake skin. Once students have a few minutes, they get neater and neater and the stiches look great!"

TOM SAYS

MEDICAL MAVERICKS

Infrared Vein Scanner

Activity

Ever had blood taken and the phlebotomist can't find your veins? They should use one of these bad boys. Students can place their arm under the device which shines an infrared light onto their arm. Different tissues, especially blood, absorb different amounts of light, changing the wavelength of light reflected back to the camera in the device. The device then converts this in to an image and projects a live video onto your arm in real time, showing you where your blood vessels are.

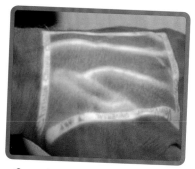

Scanning the blood vessels in the back of Barry's hand.

Careers Links
- Medical Engineer
- Phlebotomist
- Medical Imaging
- Medical Physics

Health Links
- Varicose Veins
- Diabetes
- Blood Transfusions
- Dialysis

MEDICAL MAVERICKS
TOM SAYS
MEDICAL MAVERICKS

"This is TOTES AMAZE! This device actually projects a live video of your blood vessels onto your arm so you can see where your blood vessels are. There are so many careers rolled into one here – engineering, physiology & physics!"

To book call (01902) 595 060
Or email hello@medicalmavericks.co.uk

The Careers Wall

Part of the Careers Wall we bring into the Careers in Health and Mini Medics workshops.

The Careers in Health and Mini Medics workshops both include our FAB Careers Wall. This is a series of banner stands that introduce a whole range of medical and health careers your students may not know about. These include the Top 10 Not So Well Known Careers, the Top 5 Most Common Careers, Types of Healthcare Practitioner as well as guides on how to become a Doctor, Nurse, Paramedic and Healthcare Scientist.

To book call (01902) 595 060
Or email hello@medicalmavericks.co.uk

Challenge the Champions

Who is it for?
Suitable for all age groups

How many can take part?
Up to 60 in each session

How long is it?
50-70 minutes, repeated over the day

What is it?
Ever wondered how close you could get to a professional athlete in their event? Well, in this workshop your students can compete against each other and famous athletes in a series of sports science challenges that test their strength, endurance, speed & power.

Matt testing his power output on the Watt Bike.

The challenges include:
- BATAK reaction wall
- Power output on a Watt Bike
- How far you can row in 30seconds
- Hexagon Agility Test
- Ball throwing speed
- Strength Tests
- Jump height and distance

Your students can even race a virtual Usain Bolt on The Accelerator!!! Check it out on page 215

Mitti testing his reactions and coordination on the BATAK wall.

Test 1

Hand Grip Strength

Jump Distance & Height

Test 2 & 3

Test 4

Ball Throwing Speed

The Challenges

Test 10

THE ACCELERATOR

Test 5

Rowing Distance

Test 9

Hexagon Agility

Test 7

Test 6

Whole Body Strength

Test 8

BATAK Reaction Wall

Watt Bike Power Output

Sports Hall Science PLUS

Who is it for?
GCSE, BTEC, A-Level, IBAC

How many can take part?
30-50 per session

How long is it?
Flexible, but at least 2 hours is needed.

Matt recording his respiration rate with Janet.

What is it?
Using the challenges from Challenge the Champions your students can explore **components of fitness & movement analysis** before moving onto some more in depth scientific testing that includes:

Lung Volume & Spirometry
- Respiration Rates before and after exercise
- Watt Bike Power tests
- Balance Tests

- ECG and EMG recordings
- Body Fat Analysis
- Blood Lactate Demonstrations

The can even ultrasound & see their muscles, bones, tendons, heart and blood vessels on a screen to get a better understanding of their physiology & anatomy.

James having an ultrasound of his bicep, carried out by Luke.

Race the world's greatest athletes at your school!

The Accelerator is an amazing way for your students to experience racing some of the world's greatest athletes!!

As they sprint through The Accelerator Tunnel, they race a series of lights on the floor next to them that light up at the speed of some of the greatest athletes in the world.

Their 10m sprint time is displayed on the giant leader board as they burst across the finish line, so they can see just how close (or far behind!) they were from the best!

Each student takes a score card away with their times on so they can compare themselves to friends, families and the athletes they raced.

As seen on

Tom from Medical Mavericks on Sky Sports Game Changers with Olympic Champion Darren Campbell and top 200m sprinter Christian Malcolm.

Chris, about to launch himself down The Accelerator tunnel at a major school event!

NEW!!!
The Accelerator DUEL

If racing the world's greatest athletes wasn't enough, your visitors can now race their friends and family through a 2nd tunnel next to the first.

Who will win? No one knows until they both fly out the end of their tunnels!

What you need to know

There are two versions of The Accelerator to choose from. Firstly you can choose **The Accelerator** which includes a single 10m tunnel. Or you can go for the brand new **Accelerator Dual** that includes TWO 10m tunnels, side by side, so your students can race each other!

THIS ONE IS THE MOST POPULAR!

The Accelerator – 10m singe tunnel with sprint time

New!!!

The Accelerator DUEL
Race your friends AND the greatest athletes!

This version includes **TWO tunnels side by side** so two students can race each other through their own individual tunnels. They don't see each other until they fly out the other end! Each tunnel includes their own set of racing lights and score boards at the end.

AS USED BY THESE LOVELY PEOPLE!

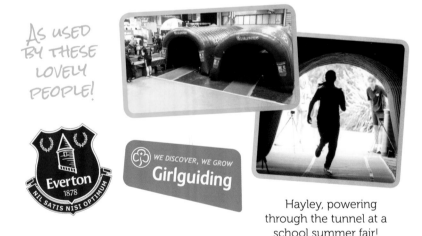

Hayley, powering through the tunnel at a school summer fair!

Olympic Champions love it!

This is what **Darren Campbell,** Olympic Champion had to say about The Accelerator when it was featured on Sky Sports Game Changers TV show.

"When I first saw The Accelerator I instantly thought, WOW! I knew it would be a big hit on the show. It is great for demonstrating reaction times & acceleration as well as why Usain Bolt is so good".

Top British Sprinter, wanted it to train on!

This is what multiple World, European & Commonwealth medalist, **Christian Malcolm** had to say about The Accelerator after trying it out with a group of children on Sky Sports Game Changers!

"The Accelerator is a great piece of equipment, something I wish I had when I was younger. It gives you a chance to test your speed against world class sprinters and gives you a gauge on how much you need to improve".

The Accelerator has been used by these organisations too!

Careers
Case Study

Jas, Kimi, Kurdeep and Mas experiencing different eye diseases with our pathology goggles.

Louise and Jane explore Colin the Colon with an endoscope.

218

Who: Denise Read

School:
Presdales School & 6th Form

Theme & Objective:
Run activities and workshops that promote the NHS as part of a wider careers day at the school that included mock interviews.

What we did:
The day started with all the pupils taking part in our Human Guinea Pig Show. This introduces them to the amazing careers in Healthcare Science with live demos and videos of Tom, the founder of Medical Mavericks having a series of medical tests performed on him! The pupils then split into three groups and visited three different Medical Mavericks workshops to try the activities from the show and more!

Denise's Feedback:
"The pupils have a much better understanding of careers in the NHS now. They absolutely loved the hands-on activities which were presented by the three best presenters of our week!! Tom and co. are excellent ambassadors for the medical careers - cheerful personalities, bright and lively characters that the pupils immediately took to and liked. They worked jolly hard and the whole event was excellent value for money. We definitely want to book them again for next year!!

"Booking Medical Mavericks helped me enormously and saved me a mountain of time. Tom Warrender inspired confidence right from the beginning that he would be reliable on the day and that he and his team would make jolly good presentations - and they did!! He and the two assistants are stars!!!"

How to book or enquire

You can call the team on **(01902) 595 060**
or email: **hello@medicalmavericks.co.uk**

219

Students can use an iPhone to take a picture
of the retina in your eye!

Taking physiological measurements such as pulse oximetry

Case Study 1

Who: Holly Aiston

School: St Anne's Catholic High School, Southampton

Theme & Objective: Year 8 science day to discover more about their own health and how the body works.

What we did: We ran three different themed workshops at the same time so we could see the whole year group at the same time. The workshop themes were careers, health and sports science. The pupils rotated round the workshops after each lesson.

Holly's Feedback: I just loved the way you just turned up, unloaded and got on with the day. You didn't ask for anything and the workshops were fantastic. The pupils got to do things they would never get to do otherwise.

Case Study 2

Who: Bob Duddridge

School: Thomas Deacon Academy, Peterborough

Theme & Objective: To promote medical and sports science to pupils as part of a week long festival for STEM.

What we did: For the TDA STEM festival we ran three different sessions. These included our Human Guinea Pig talk, a Medical Science Workshop and a Sports Science Workshop. Each day a different year group would come through the workshops to get a better insight into careers in STEM.

Bob's Feedback: *"This type of event provides a practical and relevant way to show that there is a real world where skills are needed and there are opportunities that lead from school based STEM subjects.*

"It encourages students to think about their own futures and inspires those that already have ideas but are not striving to do their best. Students came away enthused and motivated. I have always encouraged external speakers to support what we do. Hopefully more motivated and positive students will be the outcome."

How to book or enquire

You can call the team on **(01902) 595 060** or email: **hello@medicalmavericks.co.uk**

Case Study

Daniel tests his reactions on the BATAK wall.

Fred racing a virtual Usain Bolt on The Accelerator!

Who:
Pippa Taylor

School:
Oriel High School, Crawley

Theme & Objective:
Interactive workshop for year 10 to help students understand their PE & Science coursework theory.

What we did:
The day was a bespoke set of activities for their year 10 science and PE pupils. We ran a series of experiments where the pupils collected real physiological data on respiration rates, heart rates, ECGs and VO2 max tests. The also collected data from sports science performance tests such as the BATAK wall, ball throwing speed, and sprints through timing gates.

Pippa's Feedback:
"Just a little message to say a big thank you for a great work shop on Tuesday. The day ran really smoothly, and the kids really enjoyed all the activities. The team were absolutely brilliant... helpful, friendly, knew how to speak to the kids, and really know their stuff. Fab all round!

"Both the Science and PE departments have voiced a wish to use you again in the future, so would be keen to look at setting something else up next year. We also have an activities week in the summer every year, so perhaps look to use Medical Mavericks for a fun learning day linked to a subject too."

How to book or enquire
You can call the team on **(01902) 595 060** or email: **hello@medicalmavericks.co.uk**

"This is what Focus Days should be!!"

Thursday was such a good experience. I was so impressed – such a good presenter and such useful information.

The next two sessions-' Diagnostics and Surgery' and' Careers in Health' were excellent. The content was very good but what really made an impact on me was how it engaged year 11. They were involved right to the end of the sessions, there was none of the tailing off towards the end.

The presenters were very approachable and seemed to really enjoy working with the students and were willing to answer any of my questions! I looked in on the 'Challenge the Champions' session in the afternoon and the students were really enjoying themselves.

This is what a focus day should be. Several people said to me it was the best they had experienced. I don't know what went on with other year groups but this was certainly a worthwhile event. As well as informing the students about careers [beside medicine!!] they were probably not aware existed it gave them such an insight into healthcare generally – and into maintaining their own health.

**Celia Golding & Colleagues,
Langley Grammar School,
Slough**

See our

★★★★★

FaceBook Reviews

Facebook.com/MedicalMavericks

 Sarah-Jane Hope reviewed Medical Mavericks —
October 20, 2016

Absolutely fantastic! Tom and his team are wonderfully entertaining and completely knowledgeable. Our students all had a fantastic day and your Human Guinea Pig show was awesome!! Thank-you.

 Like   Comment   Share

 Kulvinder Kaur Johal reviewed Medical Mavericks —
April 2 at 9:33pm

The team are really great. They arrive early to set up and the pupils all get 2 workshops each. We book the medics every year...the yr4 team want them to come every year. The equipment they have is something you just wouldn't have in your science rooms. The children have a fabulous time and so do the staff. One year...my head teacher lay on the table and the pupils took his ECG. Unbelievable..we book them to come every March!

 Like   Comment   Share

 Kimi Bothamley reviewed Medical Mavericks —
April 1 at 1:35pm

Can't recommend these guys enough! Have had the privilege of working with them for a few years now and they have been nothing but fantastic every time. Don't stop to think if they are worth it. Just book and you will never look back.

 Like    Comment   Share

Download all 40 Posters for your Class!

You can access all 40 posters and print them off for your classroom wall to create the ultimate careers wall!

All you have to do is go to the link below and leave your details.

We will send you an email every Monday morning with a set of new posters that you can download and print for your classroom along side some fab bonus resources!

Visit www.medicalmavericks.co.uk/monday-poster-club

As a thank you we'll send you 9 posters in the post just like these!!

FREE POSTERS FOR SIGNING UP!

HOW TO BECOME A DOCTOR

START HERE

Age 18 → A-Level or IBACS Top Grades Needed!!! → **Aptitude Tests** UKCAT Or BMAT → **UCAS Application** → **Medical School Interview**

⅕ to ¼ of applicants get an interview

50% Get an offer

IMPORTANT TO CHECK
- ☑ Which Uni requires which test.
- ☑ Deadlines for sitting tests.

REMEMBER Be yourself!!!

HOW TO BECOME A NURSE

START HERE

5 x GCSEs A-C grades Maths, English & a Science Required!

THEN ONE OF THESE...

| 2-3 A-Levels Science or a health subject advised | OR | L3 Qualification BTECs Int Baccaulaureate OCR Technicals Scottish Highers | OR | Access to HE Course - 1 year with GCSEs in Maths & English |

OR

Access to HE Course

IMPORTANT – Please check with your chosen University their entry requirements.

HOW TO BECOME A HEALTHCARE SCIENTIST

START POINT FOR ALL HEALTHCARE SCIENTISTS

Option 1 - Training Route
GCSEs in Science, Maths & English Grades A-C

Option 2 - Degree Training Route
2-3 A-Levels, BTEC or L3 qualifications in sciences @ school or

Option 3 - Degree then Post Graduate
First or a 2:1 in a Biomedical or Science related degree @

HOW TO BECOME A PARAMEDIC

START HERE

5 x GCSEs A-C grades Maths, English & a Science Required!

THEN ONE OF THESE...

| 1-3 A-Levels Science or a health subject advised | OR | L3 Qualification • BTECs, HND, HNC incl a science! • Int Baccalaureate • Scottish Highers | OR | Access Course in Science or Health OR Alternative qualifications |

YOU THEN HAVE TWO CHOICES!

University Route
Course Name to Search for on UCAS: Paramedic Science

IMPORTANT – Please check with your chosen University their entry requirements. The earlier you do this the better!

Courses to choose from:

Foundation Degree — 2 Year course Full Time
Qualification: Diploma in Higher Education (or a DipHE)

BSc Degree — 3 Year course Full Time
Qualification: Bachelor of Science Degree (aka a BSc)

You then register with the Health & Care Professions Council
A full drivers license is also required with Full C1 Category that allows you to drive larger vehicles such as an ambulance!

You can now apply for Paramedic jobs
See www.jobs.nhs.uk and search for Paramedic

Starting salary around £21-22,000 moving up to £35k
with senior positions and experience over time

Student Paramedic Route
Search for Student Paramedic on www.jobs.nhs.uk

- This is an 'Earn whilst you Learn' route!
- Competition for places is high and you have to apply
- All positions for this course are advertised on the NHS Jobs Website
- Positions & availability vary between regional ambulance trusts
- Recruitment is once or twice a year!
- Drivers license required with a provisional C1 Category.
  This allows you to drive larger vehicles (no more than 3 points allowed!).
- Applicants are interviewed and go through problem solving, written, numeracy & fitness tests!

Search for Student Paramedic on www.jobs.nhs.uk
to find available positions & to find see examples of what's required

Example Training Programme
(Around £300 per month is also deducted from the below to cover course fees. BUT you do get extra pay for unsociable hours)

Level 1 - £16,677 per annum – approx 13 months

Level 2 - £19,0927 per annum – approx 9 months

Level 3 - £19,0927 per annum – 32 week University programme

Level 4 - £21,692 per annum – Achieved on course completion & registration with Health & Care Professions Council.

 facebook.com/medicalmavericks @MedicMavericks @Medical_Mavericks medicalmaverick (no 's' on the end!)

EVEN MORE RESOURCES!

To access these resources go to:
www.medicalmavericks.co.uk/free-resources

Been to a workshop

To add even more value to our workshops, there is a huge number of follow up tasks and lesson plans that you can use along side the data collected in our workshops. You can also explore what your results mean and how some of the kit works.

Careers Resources

Many of the videos from the careers section in this book, can be found in this section along side many more careers we just couldn't fit in this book!

EVEN MORE RESOURCES!

To access these resources go to:
www.medicalmavericks.co.uk/free-resources

Cool Science Stuff!

We love all science subjects and occasionally put together mini resources covering some of our favourite science experiments. Everything from Instant Ice to slinky laser sounds to bubble tennis.

Blog

If there's something topical in the news and it involves science, we are bound to cover it in our blog!

MM TV On YouTube

You can access many of our videos on careers, physiology and science in general by searching YouTube for MedicalMavericksTV

As well as hundreds of schools, these lovely people trusted us to inspire and engage their audiences and visitors with science!

To book an engaging workshop that inspires your pupils, drop us an email or call the number below

(01902) 595 060
hello@medicalmavericks.co.uk
www.medicalmavericks.co.uk

SUBSCRIBE TO
MEDICAL MAVERICKS TV
ON

Search for:
Medical Mavericks TV

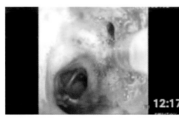

Bronchoscopy Procedure - See inside the lungs!

1.6M views · 6 years ago

12:17

Skin Prick Allergy Test

124K views · 6 years ago

4:29

DON'T FORGET TO HIT THE SUBSCRIBE BUTTON

▶ Subscribe

Want more copies of Classroom to Clinic??

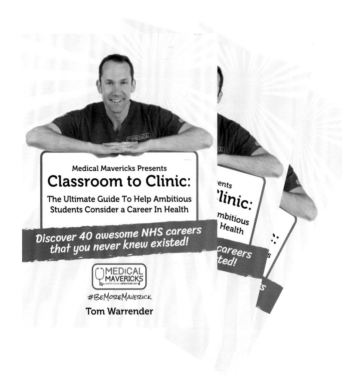

Buy them online:

www.medicalmavericks.co.uk/shop